SPACE VOLUNTEERS

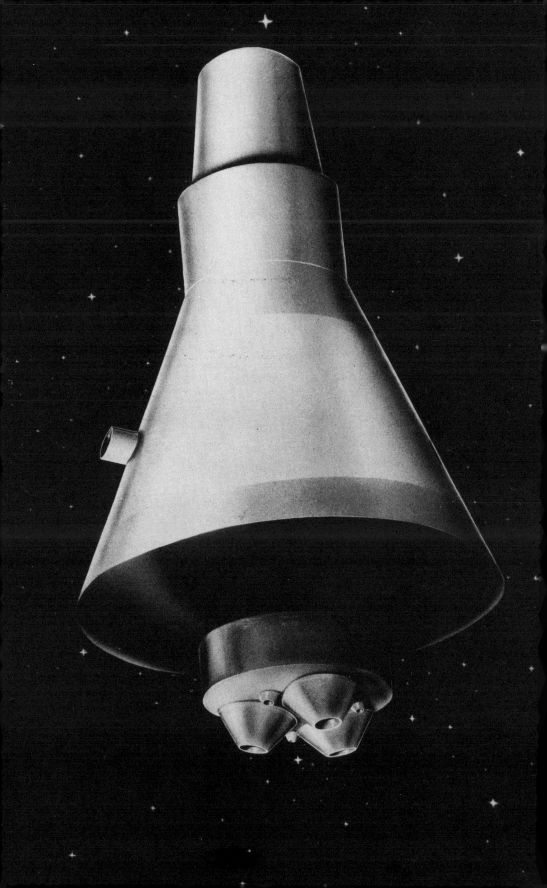

SPACE VOLUNTEERS

BY TERENCE KAY

Illustrated with photographs

HARPER & BROTHERS, NEW YORK

To my wife Dorothy
and my son Ron

CONTENTS

vii

INTRODUCTION

Man's mind, his dreams, his machines can leap the many miles to Mars, Venus and the Moon, but he must get his body there too. That is the hard part.

Across America, in jet planes, in special space chambers, in icy-cold cells and in mock-up spaceships, men are studying and solving space problems.

Every day volunteers, both scientists and others, are using their bodies to amass space facts. That man can live in outer space is being proved here on earth. Earth-bound volunteers are preparing to win the upcoming battle for space.

For years scientists have put volunteers and themselves into artificial space. It is the task of these human guinea pigs to use their minds and bodies as space testers. Tomor-

1

row's pilots and crews will know how to live in outer space, thanks to today's space pioneers.

Space volunteers are conducting experiments on a moon-like mountaintop in California; in high-riding balloons, and across antarctic wastes. They sweat in hot boxes; freeze in cold chambers; hurtle toward bone-jarring stops in rocket sleds; test moon suits and prowl beneath the polar icepack in atomic subs.

In these tests and in these places they must overcome the same kinds of hazards that the men who will fly in space and walk on other planets must face and conquer.

Space scientists know that submarines are similar to spaceships. Like a spaceship, the undersea craft glides through a hostile world, for the restless sea is forever trying to force its way into the intruder's steel hull. Just as submarines do now, spaceships will carry their own bit of earth with them —their own food, water, heat and air.

In outer space one false move, one mechanical or human error can cause disaster. Under the sea a submarine crew member opens the wrong valve and tons of sea water rush in to flood the ship. A rocketship crew member turns the wrong valve 900,000 miles out from earth, and the spaceship's air supply gushes out into the surrounding vacuum.

The atomic sub *Nautilus* pushes through the murky ocean beneath the North Pole, but if the ship's sonar unit fails the sub will crash into a projecting ice shelf. If a spaceship's radarscope fails the space vehicle might smash into an asteroid.

An atomic submarine's crew travels sealed inside the ship's steel hull for weeks, even months. How do the men

2

take it? Knowing what happens to men confined in a small area for so long a period tells space scientists how spacemen, locked in their ship, will take the long space voyage.

Scientists working and living in the thin air of California's White Mountain are preparing spacemen for excursions on the planets and the airless moon.

Men mush across the antarctic's snowy whiteness, testing themselves and their clothing against the punishing cold. Antarctic temperatures will be encountered in space: on the moon and on the planets.

Scientists reason that if man can stand the cold, the bleakness and the loneliness of the antarctic he can withstand the rigors of life on the moon.

A balloon rider floats high into earth's upper reaches. Each hour that he lives on the fringe of space he adds valuable data to man's knowledge as he learns more about dangerous cosmic rays and unlocks dozens of other space secrets.

The rocketsled slams to a sudden stop; the rider's body strains against the holding straps. He is testing spaceman's reaction to abrupt spaceship stops.

Perched atop an "Iron Cross" inside a test lab a man begins another "dry run." He is practicing how to maneuver a ship in outer space. Because a volunteer is "piloting" the weird, crosslike contraption spacemen will know how to guide their speeding ships.

A volunteer suffers and sweats inside a "hot box." Hundreds of powerful lights glare down upon him while he struggles to keep his mind on flying an imaginary spaceship. He is showing scientists how much heat a space pilot will be able to take and still get his ship safely back to earth.

Other men stride around test labs in moon suits. Locked inside cold, airless cells they pretend they are on the moon, and attempt to learn as much about that heavenly body as if they were actually on it.

At 100,000 feet the test pilot pushes the jet's throttle to full power. He is young enough to be one of the lucky ones who will make the switch from airplanes to spaceplanes to spaceships. As he "wrings out" the latest jet he remembers that one day he will head a rocketship off this planet.

Space Day, 19—. The first man-carrying spaceship blasts off. The pilot and crew are better prepared for their voyage than any men for any voyage in history.

They will face many perils as they streak through space, but they will defeat them. For their way will be prepared by the heroic efforts of a long line of space volunteers.

This is a book about those space volunteers.

1 EIGHTY THOUSAND MILES OUT

Thousands of miles in outer space trouble crept unseen upon Dalton Smith, Jr. Deadly carbon-dioxide fumes were flooding his cramped spaceship cabin. The nineteen-year-old youth's head dropped drowsily on his T-shirted chest.

Eighteen hours of sitting alone in a sealed cabin had numbed his senses and made him sleepy. But this was a different drowsiness, it spelled danger. Smith's tired senses could not warn him that he had somehow knocked off the hose leading to the cabin's carbon-dioxide absorber. The absorber changed the poisonous air expelled by his lungs into pure, life-giving oxygen. Now as Smith exhaled carbon dioxide he diluted the oxygen in the chamber. Each time he exhaled it meant there was less oxygen for him to breathe. In moving about the furnace-size cubicle he had

1. Dalton Smith, Jr., sits in the simulated spaceship in which he made an 80,000-mile trip into space without leaving earth.

bumped the hose connection, and the absorber was useless.

His head jerked up; he groaned in protest. Somewhere, as in a dream, he could hear a record playing a singsong of odd words:

"Smitty, connect . . ." Then the song faded. He strained to hear. Something told him to listen.

"Smitty, connect the CO_2 absorber. Smitty, connect the CO_2—" He moaned and shook the cobwebs from his brain.

6

2. Keeping in touch with **Smith are** Captain Emanuel Roth and Dr. James Gaume. Furnace-like simulator is at extreme right.

The record cut off. Now he knew it wasn't a record—it was Dr. Gaume. It was the firm, real voice of Dr. Gaume talking to him on the intercom.

"It's connected, sir," Smith said into his end of the intercom. He remembered connecting the absorber and checking it before take-off.

"Check it, Smitty."

Sleepily the youth reached down. His groping fingers found the connection—it *was* broken! He closed his fingers

7

over the mechanism and refastened it. Slowly he began to feel better. His drowsiness faded away. He breathed in deeply, drawing in more life-giving oxygen. He sat up straighter on the canvas seat, and grinned. He felt better now.

Outside the sealed steel cubicle the anxious look left the faces of Drs. James Gaume and Emanuel Roth, who had watched the whole ordeal through the cabin's portholes. Dr. Roth studied the gauges, which showed that Smith's pulse and respiration were slowly returning to normal. Dr. Gaume checked his watch: "He's well past his eighteenth hour, the experiment's going splendidly."

"Another six hours," observed Dr. Roth, "and Smitty will be back on earth."

Standing outside the space cabin simulator, Dr. Hubertus Strughold, director of the Air Force's Department of Space Medicine, looked at his watch. The hands pointed to exactly 3:00 P.M. The space doctor nodded and Drs. Roth and Gaume opened the cabin door. For the first time in twenty-four hours the door to the outside world swung wide for Dalton Smith.

Smith rose slowly from his canvas chair, then stepped across the threshold. As TV cameras ground, Dr. Strughold asked the boy:

"How do you feel, Smitty?"

"Fine, sir."

"Are you ready for the three-day trip to the moon?"

"Yes, sir," Smith said with a smile, "just give me a night's sleep first."

8

Nineteen-year-old Dalton Smith, one of our youngest space volunteers, is an Air Force man. His official title is aeromedical technician, but actually he is a human guinea pig, one of the hundreds of men who are rolling back the space curtain.

Smith made the long, lonely trip in the cramped cabin to help space science. During the twenty-four hours he was sealed in the airtight cabin he traveled 80,000 miles, or one third of the way to the moon. And he made the journey without ever leaving the ground. For the test took place at the Department of Space Medicine of the School of Aviation Medicine, Randolph Air Force Base, Texas. Smith forced himself to sit for twenty-four hours straight in a simulated space cabin to withstand many of the same conditions that a rocketship pilot may someday encounter on a flight to the moon.

The metal cylinder, or space cabin simulator, in which "pilot" Smith lived, gave him an exact likeness of our earth's complicated atmosphere and served six other functions:

One: The cabin was kept at a constant air pressure similar to that in which we live.

Two: The cabin was supplied with the oxygen the pilot required.

Three: A carbon-dioxide absorber in the cubicle took away all the toxic CO_2 that Smith exhaled.

Four: Moisture given off in breathing and perspiring was taken away.

Five: Smith's body temperature was kept from rising to dangerous heights.

Six: The space simulator automatically reduced the

9

amount of heat striking it from the outside. This is very important because a spaceship will encounter fierce heat from solar radiation and from friction as it flies out and back through the earth's atmosphere.

With each grueling experiment to which they subject their bodies Smith and the other brave volunteers are bringing closer the day of safe space flight.

Scientists the world over agree that within a few years man will have rocketed to our moon and back. One day a projectile will scream out from earth and course through the black void of space. Inside the vehicle will sit a pilot and his crew who will pit their fragile bodies against all the horrors, known and unknown, of outer space.

Spacemen must be shielded from all the dangers lurking out beyond earth. What would happen if the sealed space cabin sprang a leak? How will the crew react to being locked in their space cocoon? Will the long, tedious hours, the loneliness, drive them crazy? What will happen to the men when they are under the constant bombardment of cosmic rays—rays about which we know so little?

And what about the earliest feeling of all—weightlessness, when the spaceman's coffee floats up from his cup and his body rises out of his seat if he is not securely strapped down? How will the spacemen take all this?

We must find the answers to these and other perplexing problems. The only way to unlock the secrets of space is to make believe man is actually traveling in space. That means putting human volunteers through the same dangers that occur in space and seeing if they can live through them.

This is why young men such as Dalton Smith are sitting

in icy-cold, high-altitude chambers, riding speeding rock-etsleds across burning desert sands, soaring high above the earth beneath flimsy plastic bags, and sitting in simulated space cabins.

The volunteers are using their bodies to find the answers scientists must have before the first manned spaceship blasts off through the last frontier.

2 FASTEST MEN ON EARTH

X minus 30. A siren wailed across the New Mexico desert. Air Force and Northrop Aircraft Company technicians, checking the rocketsled, worked faster. For five sweating hours they had been making sure that nothing would go wrong. For weeks before these final thirty minutes they had been laboring to make the sled as safe as possible.

In the underground blockhouse 100 feet from the sled scientists and technicians watched the feverish activity through periscopes. A blue Air Force ambulance drew up in a swirl of desert dust and waited in readiness near the track.

X minus 16. In sixteen minutes the test sled and its rider would blast down the track at more than 400 miles per hour.

Seconds after blasting off the sled would come to an abrupt, bone-jarring stop.

Scientist and Flight Surgeon Lieutenant Colonel John P. Stapp strode to the bright red sled. His medium-built frame showed nervousness in many ways. He could see the ambulance waiting near the 2,000-foot-long track; if anything went wrong it would take his battered body to the Holloman Air Force Base Hospital.

"One of America's bravest men," they had called him, "riding one of the most dangerous vehicles in the United States." The volunteer climbed into the sled's aircraft-type seat. On this, his twenty-seventh run, he didn't feel like a brave man, he was remembering other decelerator sled runs.

He thought of the time the sled's quick stop had fractured his rib. Riding the high-speed sled into the water brakes was like driving a car 120 miles per hour into a brick wall, and Flight Surgeon Stapp recalled the time the roaring sled had broken his arm. On other runs he had suffered a moderate concussion, plus bleeding of the eye retina. Several rocket rides had given him headaches and stiff muscles. But Colonel Stapp insisted that the deceleration experiments must go on; he wanted to learn all he could about the effects of sudden stops on a man's body.

"X minus 10," thundered the loud-speaker. The colonel thought of the sled run before this when violent headaches had gripped him for two days after the ride and he had been partially blind for twelve long days. But he was all right now.

The technicians finished strapping him into the seat. One,

13

two red flares skyrocketed up from alongside the block-house. Two minutes to go. The technicians stepped back and all eyes focused on the volunteer and the powerful test carriage.

Two minutes ticked off. Smoke puffed out behind the sled. Then the rockets let go in a flaming, roaring surge of power, blasting the vehicle and its passenger down the track faster than any man had ever traveled across the face of the earth.

Moments later, at the opposite end of the track, water geysered 100 feet high, as the rear sled's scoop hit the water brake. Smashing into the water brake at 421 miles per hour the sled separated into two sections.

The forward sled, containing Colonel Stapp, whizzed on alone another 200 feet. Water spouted skyward as it slammed into the last water brake.

Observers watched the rider's body jerk forward against the seat's holding straps, then back. Technicians ran to the sled, and an Air Force doctor unbuckled the nylon binding bands.

The colonel grinned. "I feel fine now," he told them, "the sled's a wonderful test instrument. I'm ready to go again this afternoon."

Why did Colonel Stapp submit his body to the agonies of sudden stops?

"It's important," he explained, "because on completion of the tests I'll have a perfect graph of the survival force limits of the human body. It's never been done, and it must be done." Then Colonel Stapp summed up his feelings and those of many other devoted earth-bound spacemen: "In

14

3. Colonel John Stapp signals a happy double "O" as he completes a successful run on the rocket sled.

research, once you start you can't stop. Tests have proved that the human body, sometimes believed to be as fragile as an egg, has almost unbelievable ability to withstand shocks under certain circumstances."

In space flight man will need all the strength he can muster to withstand bone-shattering shocks. Time and again his body will be subjected to sudden stopping action as he returns his rocketship through the braking effect of earth's air blanket.

When Colonel Stapp made his twenty-seventh rocket sled run in 1954 he hit 421 miles per hour. Two years later he roared down the desert track at 632 miles per hour.

One moment his rocket-powered vehicle was zipping down the steel track at 632 miles per hour. A second and a half later the sled slammed to a full stop—halted by the world's most powerful braking system.

Except for a plastic helmet with a clear plastic visor to protect his face, Colonel Stapp wore no special clothing. The wind smashed against him at full force. The air blast was equal to 1.7 times the speed of sound. Both his eyes were blackened during the 632-miles-per-hour ride, for the sudden stop threw his eyeballs forward against his eyelids.

The many cruel rides took their toll and at length the Air Force "grounded" Colonel Stapp because he was too valuable to risk his life in further high-speed experiments. Since then he has overseen many tests by other brave men and is devoting his life to preventing injuries and death in aircraft crashes and to seeking safe means of space travel.

Colonel Stapp's sled is actually two vehicles: a propulsion sled, weighing about 3,500 pounds, and the test sled itself, which weighs 2,000 pounds. The propulsion sled can carry up to twelve rockets, but the most Colonel Stapp ever used was nine. The nine rockets develop a thrust equal to 40,000 pounds and are ignited by remote control from the blockhouse.

The test sled runs on strong, extra-heavy railroad tracks

4. Riding the decelerator rocket sled Colonel Stapp blasts down the track at more than 400 miles per hour.

placed on a concrete bed. Standard tracks are located five feet apart; the test tracks are spaced seven feet apart and weigh twice as much as standard rails. The sled slides along the tracks on metal sliders—or "slippers"—instead of wheels.

Between the tracks runs a trough 5 feet wide and 18 inches deep. Water used to stop the sled is stored in the trough. Beneath each of the two sleds are large metal scoops. As the speeding sled passes over the water the scoops hit the water bringing the vehicle to an abrupt halt.

Colonel Stapp leads the volunteer rocket sled tester team which includes Captain Vincent Mazza, Captain David Mahoney, Master Sergeant Lawrence Lambert, Master Sergeant James F. Ferguson, Technical Sergeant William A.

17

Rhea, Staff Sergeant Richard H. Allgire, and Corporal Raymond L. Leach.

After each grueling ride aeromedical doctors put the sled volunteers through a series of tests which show exactly how well the riders' bodies took the abrupt stop.

Rocketsled experimenters are not daredevils. They sit strapped to the dangerous sled and rocket toward bone-jarring stops so that the men who will fly high-altitude jet aircraft, spaceplanes and spaceships may live.

3   GRAVITY CHEATERS

Space project engineer Dr. Edwin Vail, clothed in a space suit and helmet, tumbled helplessly about the big cabin of the Air Force C-130 transport plane. Now he floated upside down, his feet nearly touching the cabin ceiling and his head dangling almost to the floor, yet he felt as though he was standing right side up. Twenty seconds later he spun backward, his body slammed against the side of the cabin and slithered to the floor. The C-130 had completed the weightless part of its flight. Dr. Vail was once more a passenger in a normal-flying plane, but for almost a minute he had been experiencing the same condition a man in space will feel—the unique feeling of weighing absolutely nothing.

In other flights using the huge plane Major Edward Brown and Lieutenant Melvin Gardner of the Air Force's

19

Wright Air Development Center, Dayton, Ohio, used magnetic shoes to "stand" on the aircraft's ceiling. Throughout the C-130's weightlessness maneuver they felt as though they were standing on the floor. The pilot and the accompanying photographer were strapped to their seats to prevent them from floating upside down.

Zero gravity, or weightlessness, is one of the eeriest of all the sensations man will have to contend with in space. It is also one of the most dangerous.

Suppose you have just blasted off the earth as a crew member in a spaceship. You have suffered the agonies of acceleration and now you begin to experience the phenomenon of weightlessness. The ship is now about 120 miles out and has begun orbiting around the globe. Suddenly everything in the ship, including you, mysteriously weighs absolutely nothing.

There is no up and no down. The familiar pull of gravity, a force you have lived with all your life, is gone, for now there is no gravity. Air in the space vehicle will not circulate. You breathe faster trying to suck in oxygen. Has the ship sprung a leak? you wonder. You start to suffocate because the air will not circulate. You have always breathed in air through your nose, now you have an airless space in front of your nose and mouth. The surrounding atmosphere is motionless and cannot flow in to fill the empty space.

While you twist your head, seeking another mouthful of oxygen, the ship's fans whir into action. Air begins to flow into your lungs as the special fans force oxygen to circulate through the craft. Breathing is no longer a problem.

20

You and the other crew members are strapped to your seats because you would float in mid-air if you were not lashed down. Coffee and other liquids would float in the spaceship cabin if they were served in cups or glasses, so you eat and drink liquid food and water through tubes inserted in plastic squeeze-type containers.

In this gravity zero state your limbs move in jerks until they are accustomed to the odd sensation. Your brain may become befuddled. If the space vehicle gets into difficulty, will you and the other crew members react in time and wisely enough to cope with the danger?

These are a few of the fearsome problems astronauts must solve during the long period of weightlessness. Many more, perhaps worse, obstacles face space crews during this phase of their trip.

Scientists must try to find out all the possible zero-gravity problems that the spacemen will encounter; then they must discover the solutions. They must do this now, and that is why man needs to practice living in the weird world of weightlessness.

It is hard to achieve zero gravity here on earth because gravity is everywhere. Down through the ages the unseen force of gravity has locked man upon his planet; even airplanes cannot repulse gravity's pull. Now man is finally beating gravity if only for a brief time—only for about 45 seconds in airborne craft and somewhat longer in laboratory experiments. Soon he may defeat the mighty force that has kept him earth-bound for hundreds of thousands of years.

One of the dreams of space scientists is to make a rocket-ship which can neutralize the force of gravity, but they are not waiting for such a vehicle to be perfected. Man is determined to conquer space and will not be denied, so he works at making the weightlessness phenomenon right here on earth.

Streaking high above Texas jet pilot Major Herbert Stallings spoke into the intercom: "The ship is ready, Doc." "Start the run," answered Dr. Siegfried Gerathewohl from the cockpit's rear seat.

Stallings fed more power to the F-94 jet. Picking up speed, the Air Force plane began its trajectory across the sky. As the jet streaked through its arc Dr. Gerathewohl worked at his experiments. He was studying the effects of weightlessness on a spaceship pilot's co-ordination.

Major Stallings and Dr. Gerathewohl, a civilian in the Air Force's School of Aviation Medicine, were trying to capture for a few moments the sensation of weightlessness or zero gravity. Complete weightlessness is a feeling entirely foreign to earth-clinging man, who never experiences the sensation of weighing absolutely nothing. The major and the doctor were flying their "gravity-cheating" arc to manufacture this unearthly feeling for space science.

In forty-five seconds the experiment was over. At present writing man can achieve the feeling of being totally weightless for only seconds but faster planes will make longer periods of "gravity cheating" possible. Rocketplanes, such as the X-15, will be able to make a pilot weightless for from five to ten minutes.

The two investigators and Dr. Edwin Vail in the C-130 "stole" their twenty to forty-five seconds of zero gravity by flying the umbrella-shaped arc known as the Keplerian trajectory. The arc is named after the famous astronomer, Johann Kepler, who proved that planets orbit through the universe in a gigantic, many-million-mile arc of this type. Artillery shells also whiz from gun muzzle to target in the same kind of arc or trajectory.

The phenomenon of weightlessness was first observed during World War II by Dr. Heinz von Diringshofen, a German professor. Two German scientists, Dr. Otto Gauer and Dr. Heinz Haber, realizing that it would hamper space flight, put their minds to work on the zero-gravity problem. The most startling fact they learned was that weightlessness might affect the brain. They also discovered that the best way for man to overcome the weightless state was by flying a Keplerian trajectory.

Some years later the United States Air Force wanted to conduct weightlessness studies and asked Dr. Haber and his brother to join the Department of Space Medicine at the Air Force School of Aviation Medicine near San Antonio, Texas.

In 1951 the experiments began. Scott Crossfield, one of the world's most famous test pilots, was the first guinea pig. Crossfield made fifty flights over the California desert, and in about thirty of his trajectories produced true zero-gravity conditions. At about the same time another well-known test pilot, Major Charles E. Yeager, was flying zero-gravity flights out of the same airbase. Yeager said that in his thirteenth second of weightlessness he felt as though he was slowly spinning around, but in what direction he did not know. Of course he was actually doing no such thing but was flying straight as an arrow.

More than a hundred men have taken zero-gravity rides as passengers in jets flown by Crossfield, Yeager, and the champion of weightlessness flying, Major Stallings. About 50 per cent of the riders said the sensation was "the most wonderful experience" they had ever had. Others complained that a feeling of "befuddlement" overcame them and that had they not been strapped to the jet's seat and blindfolded "disorientation might have become extreme."

Air Force technicians at Wright Air Development Center pressed a blindfold tightly across the volunteer's eyes and over his head they placed a diving helmet. Then they lowered him gently into the glass-walled tank, cloudy with salt water, where he was strapped to a special chair whose legs had been welded to the tank's bottom. Once immersed in the salt water, or brine, the man was weightless, for the water was salty enough to be of the same specific gravity as the volunteer's body.

At a signal the weightlessness experiment utilizing man's buoyancy under water began. From their positions outside the tank the technicians were able to move the chair; they tilted it at a sharp angle and then asked the volunteer which way the chair was tipped. He insisted through the intercom that his chair had not been tilted at all, but that he was sitting straight.

Later the blindfold was removed and the underwater volunteer was given a number of tasks to perform, such as moving various levers and pushing buttons near the chair.

24

5. This strange contraption is one of the newest weightlessness testers. Compressed air raises the volunteer, who is strapped to the bed. The bed moves in three directions.

It was found that weightlessness seriously affected his control of the levers. However, the more he practiced moving the levers the better he could do it. Next he was submerged upside down in the tank. It made no difference; he worked the controls equally well whether he was sitting right side up or was upside down.

In another WADC experiment airmen are learning about weightlessness by going to bed. The latest type zero-gravity experiments are conducted on a platform upon which a mesh bed is mounted. The platform contains its own compressed air which is blown downward out of the bottom, thereby making the platform float freely on a column of air. The volunteer is first strapped to the mesh bed. He is then asked to work airplane-type controls to find out how good his co-ordination is and how well he can perform the task in a weightless state. With the free-moving weightlessness simulator a man can experience zero-gravity conditions

6. Weightlessness problem: a volunteer wearing an XMC-2 full-pressure suit tries to reach the controls of the air-bearing platform on which he is standing. As he moves toward the controls they turn away from him.

for a much longer period of time than he can by the aircraft method.

The Air Force volunteer's body tenses inside his XMC-2 full-pressure suit as he stands on the air-jet disk. Making sure his feet are firmly planted on the two-foot-wide disk, he suddenly twists the rest of his body in one quick movement. The disk, supported only by a powerful jet of compressed air, spins round and round. The slightest movement causes the air-supported disk to spin like a top. The ingenious disk is another device WADC is using to explore some of the problems of weightlessness.

Spaceship-type control panels are placed in a circle waist high and within arm's reach of the volunteer. When a signal light flashes on one of the control panels he reaches for the control as quickly as he can and moves the lever. When a control panel at one side or behind him lights up he must be careful not to move too fast, for quick movement causes the disk to spin around past the control. In a spaceship, where split-second timing in working control levers will be important, this could prove fatal. As day after day he continues to ride the disk the volunteer becomes more skillful in reaching for and working the controls. And when the first astronaut heads for space he too will know how to control his ship as he "cheats gravity."

4 SPACE INVADERS

Lonely and dangerous was the man's mission. Air Force Captain J. W. Kittinger, Jr., sat alone, sealed inside a cocoonlike capsule 96,000 feet above the Minnesota countryside. A gigantic, yet fragile, balloon whose sides were about as thin as this paper was all that kept him from plunging to earth 18 miles below.

For an hour and fifty minutes the space volunteer hovered on the other side of the new frontier. Sitting there in outer space he knew he had crossed over into a new world. Could he get back? That depended upon many things. First, on his own courage—he must not allow panic to overtake him in this strange place; panic could mean death. Second, he had to depend on the skill of the men who made the great white bag suspending him at the frontier of space. If the balloon broke, Captain Kittinger would plunge to his death.

Third, there was the weather. At lower altitudes vicious thunderstorms could dash the balloon and its man-carrying gondola to bits on the ground miles below. Fourth, his oxygen-making machine must be kept in perfect working order.

But Captain Kittinger had no time to think of his danger, he had to look after the rows of instruments which lined the inside of the 8-by-3-foot gondola. The instruments were recording various kinds of information, such as cosmic-ray strength and the mental and physical effects of high altitudes on human beings. Captain Kittinger had volunteered to see what would happen to a man suspended in space. The new science of space biology needed to know this.

On June 2, 1957, the Air Force captain spent twelve hours in the sealed capsule. It took that long for the helium-filled balloon to lift the brave volunteer 18 miles up and to bring him down to earth again. Captain Kittinger's trip proved to be routine, but sometime before this two Navy skyriders, probing the hostile regions above our world, got the scare of their lives.

South Dakota's Black Hills grew misty as the 100-foot-long Skyhook balloon ascended. Inside the airtight gondola swinging gently beneath the balloon Lieutenant Commander Malcolm Ross and Lieutenant Commander Morton Lewis shook hands. "Project Stratolab" was under way.

The Navy meteorologists rose slowly upward. They would not start back until their plastic bag had lifted them 76,000 feet above the earth. At that height, and during their ascent and descent, they were testing their reactions to high altitudes.

Time: 6:19 A.M., November 8, 1956. The powerful lifting action of helium pushing against the balloon's sides forced the 67-foot-wide bag to soar steadily. The volunteers studied their altimeter. Just before 9:00 A.M. the needle showed 75,000 feet. Now the automatic gas valve should begin to release enough gas to keep the balloon at that altitude.

Ross and Lewis began making their final tests. But something had gone wrong. Like a wild, uncontrolled thing the balloon spurted upward a full thousand feet.

Then the automatic gas valve opened, letting out too much helium. The plastic bag began to go down, and fast. Hastily the two men strapped themselves to their seats. The altimeter needle showed they were dropping 3,000 feet per minute.

They looked up, but they could not see the balloon. A sickening feeling swept over them. Had the bag burst? Was the heavy gondola plunging earthward like a stone? Commander Lewis punched the microphone button of their radio and spoke to the Navy cover plane flying somewhere below the cloud layer.

"We're falling," he shouted. "Feels like the balloon is gone."

Thousands of feet below, the cover plane, actually a flying medical laboratory, was busy recording the balloonists heart and lung reactions. The balloon's radio was fixed so that only one person could talk over it at a time. At that helpless moment the plane's captain, who could neither see the balloon nor hear of the men's plight, was saying, "Congratulations on reaching desired altitude."

Commander Lewis kept calling that he and Commander Ross were in trouble. Because the captain had been talking to the balloonists he could not hear them, and he repeated, "Congratulations."

Ross began punching the ballast release button. Steel shot dropped from the gondola, but still it continued plunging down, down, like a high-speed elevator. There was one thing in their favor. They had not lost the balloon; it still bulged intact above the gondola.

In all Ross dropped 300 pounds of shot. By that time the balloon was floating at 38,000 feet. Lessening the weight by 300 pounds helped to slow the speed of the descent but they were still falling at a rate of 1,400 feet per minute. To land the balloon at that speed would probably mean death.

The men started to loosen all the equipment in the gondola—oxygen tanks, instruments, panels, the radio. To lighten the load they were prepared to toss out everything not nailed down.

Now they floated at 17,000 feet. Ross checked the pressure gauge. The needle showed that the air pressure inside and outside the sealed gondola was equal. That was a good sign. Each man opened an escape hatch and without a word began to toss out everything that was loose.

The bag's wild plunge was halted. The riders took heart, as the rate of dropping slowed to 1,000 feet per minute—900 feet—800—600. Their chances looked brighter, for at 600 to 800 feet per minute a fairly safe landing could be made.

The skyriders gazed out to the horizon, which showed

"fiery white." As they looked upward toward the heavens the sky changed before their eyes, turning gradually to light blue and then to darker blue. Right above them the sky appeared a velvet black, yet all the time the sun streamed into their gondola.

Finally, when they were a scant 30 feet aboveground, the balloon slowed to safe landing speed, and the skyclimbers eased onto the ground unharmed.

After they had had a brief rest the Navy put the two volunteers through thirty physical tests to determine what effects drifting 76,000 feet above the earth had on the human system.

The balloon riders were not new to the higher altitudes. On their first "Project Stratolab," a few months prior to this almost fatal trip, they had soared to 40,000 feet in an open-space laboratory. They were the first men to go so high in an open basket.

Special cold-weather suits equipped with oxygen masks protected their bodies during the open-air ride. Without space-tailored suits they might well have frozen to death, for at 40,000 feet the temperature stood at 70 degrees below zero.

Describing the open-air trip Ross said, "You have no sensation of moving along. Above the clouds was nothing, nothing but the sheer beauty of the sky, from light blue to royal blue. We could look down and see the earth where the clouds broke; it looked real patchy."

Another "plastic bag rider" who almost rode to his death was Air Force Major David Simons. Simons's flight beyond the earth's protective air blanket began 425 feet below the level of the ground.

At an Air Force base near Minneapolis the major was sealed into a capsule no bigger than a telephone booth. Then capsule and spaceman were taken 150 miles by truck to an open-pit mine, 425 feet deep, in the Mesabi iron range. The Air Force chose this strange launching area because the air in the pit was much more still than the air above the ground, and the balloon could begin its ascent in a calm atmosphere.

In the pit technicians began pumping helium into the 3,000,000-cubic-foot capacity polyethylene bag while the

7. Plastic balloon is inflated for Major Simons's 102,000-foot ascent to the frontier of space. Gondola is at far left.

(U.S. AIR FORCE)

plastic balloon, now bulging fat with helium, strained at its leashes. Everything had been checked and double-checked. The flight to the edge of space was ready to begin. A breeze that could grow into a dangerous wind fluttered the workmen's clothes.

"Let her go!" ordered Otto Winzen, the balloon's maker. Slowly the huge white shape rose from the pit. Inside the aluminum gondola suspended many feet below the bag, David Simons felt no sensation of rising. Then, seconds later, a gentle lifting feeling came to him.

He watched through his capsule's observation ports as the mine's rocky walls slipped past. He knew that a wind could dash his fragile bag against those jagged walls, but he put that thought out of his mind and turned to his work. He had twenty-five experiments to do.

Crammed with him inside the 3-by-8-foot capsule were balloon controls, an altimeter, banks of instruments, temperature and pressure gauges, cameras, a 5-inch telescope, a tape recorder, food, drugs, and many other items.

Simons wore a high-altitude pressure suit to protect him in case anything went wrong with the capsule. Photographic plates were taped to his arms and chest to register cosmic rays. When Simons returned to the ground the doctors would study the photographs and examine him over a period of years to determine what effect the mysterious but penetrating cosmic rays had on a human being.

Also taped to the volunteer's chest was a stethoscope which radioed his heartbeat to his commanding officer, rocketsled rider Colonel John Stapp, on the ground below. The sound of Simons's heartbeat came to Colonel Stapp as a beep signal, similar to beeps sent out by earth satellites.

Hour after hour the balloon pushed steadily into the upper regions. Although clouds hid the bag from ground-party viewers, they could follow its flight on their radar screens. As the balloon drifted west across the Minnesota sky the ground crew motored after it in trucks and trailers. After a time Otto Winzen, who had been talking by radio with Major Simons, began to be concerned.

"David," he called, "your voice and breathing are no longer being received." The man in the balloon seemed to be in danger, but the men on the ground left to him the decision as to whether he should come down to safety or stay up with danger.

Colonel Stapp radioed, "I leave it up to you, David."

"Sir," came Simons's reply, "I want to stay up." He still had a number of experiments to finish.

Midnight. Cold crept into the high-riding capsule and weariness came over Simons. Then Colonel Stapp's voice rattled his earphones, "Have you eaten yet?" Simons jerked up his head in surprise; why, he had completely forgotten about food. Stapp advised him to eat a couple of candy bars.

Morning, and 76,000 feet up. As the sun's rays made the gas expand, the balloon began rising. By 8:00 A.M. the 100-foot-long bag had soared to 90,000 feet. Far below lurked ugly, black thunderclouds. The space-fringing vehicle had veered southwest. Simons now floated over South Dakota, and one of Dakota's fearsome summer storms muttered and growled at his feet.

Ten A.M. Simons saw the first break in the weather. High

35

over Aberdeen, South Dakota, the boiling clouds parted, leaving a hole straight down to the earth 90,000 feet below. Looking westward through the portholes he could make out the Missouri River snaking south.

Major Simons had been sealed in the cramped capsule for thirty-six hours, twenty-four of them in the sky. Aches throbbed through his body—it must be time to come down.

But now Otto Winzen ordered him to stay up because rushing past the cloud opening at a lower level was a jet stream whose powerful current could snatch the downward-drifting balloon and hurl it right into the thunderstorm. The bag's walls were thinner than a razor blade and in a windstorm they would be torn to shreds.

Simons thought of his parachute, but he dared not hit the silk at so awesome a height. To leap out into the rarefied air and drop into that rough, tough thunderstorm would be suicide.

The ground crew, following the balloon across the Dakota plains, radioed directions to him. They were trying to pinpoint his location above the clouds. They had noticed that for some strange reason the major was giving a false bearing of his position. Colonel Stapp was alarmed because Simons spoke over the ground-to-balloon radio at only a fourth his usual speed, and his voice continued to slow down.

A weary, slow-talking, slow-breathing Simons heard the radioed instructions: "Check the capsule's CO_2 level," Colonel Stapp was saying. The major checked; the carbon dioxide had risen to the danger point.

Ground crew member Captain Archibald radioed quickly: "Clamp on pressure suit mask—breathe pure oxy-

36

gen." Simons's fingers pressed the oxygen mask to his face. He sucked in pure oxygen from the emergency supply. The capsule's air regenerator began to remove some of the backed-up CO_2.

Fifteen minutes later he took the mask off. The atmosphere was safe now, but the air regenerator absorbed the CO_2 so slowly that he had to repeat the operation over and over. As Simons struggled with the oxygen supply the balloon suddenly began to rise. Before the skyrider realized it the altimeter showed that he was at 96,000 feet. He valved gas, but the plastic bag kept its altitude.

Another dial showed him a new danger. The capsule's battery power was running so low that Simons had to cut off his cooling system. In minutes the temperature rose to 84 degrees. To his body aches came the added suffering of heat. He knew that a man sealed in a pressure suit could not long stand temperatures above 80 degrees.

Each time CO_2 began filling the capsule Simons had to clamp on his oxygen mask. This made him feel even hotter. But he must not panic—panic could doom him. If he had not been a trained physician he might have lost control, but he was a scientist and knew the reasons for his feeling of near-frenzy. He knew that too much carbon dioxide causes panic in persons who are confined in a small space.

As the bag pushed higher—it finally reached 102,000 feet, a new world's altitude record—the sun's warm rays bore down on the sealed capsule. The heat became more and more unbearable. Simons gave himself a stern talking to, he must keep his wits about him, he must not crack. Locked alone in the gondola, floating in the hostile, edge-of-space

37

world his only chance of survival was to keep calm.

Far below Otto Winzen paced back and forth. At last he found the answer. "Valve off more gas," he instructed Simons; "the cool air rushing past your falling capsule will cool it."

Simons began valving gas. Through the ports he saw an opening in the black clouds below. It was a beautiful, wide, clear break. At first the balloon refused to drop lower. Then, at 95,000 feet, it began sliding down but the rider had not reckoned with the sun's heat. The lower the gas bag drifted the more heat it picked up. The heat expanded the helium, and with its sides bulging the balloon started off for the higher regions. Between 11:45 A.M. and 1:40 P.M the plastic shape rose and fell like a giant yo-yo.

Finally, at 89,000 feet, the bag would not move. Was there no way down? Simons twisted in his seat, trying to ignore the aches in his body and his growing fatigue. What strange force held his high-riding vehicle up he did not know.

Time: 2:16 P.M. At last the balloon started a steady downward voyage.

Time: 5:32 P.M. Forty-two hours and fifty-two minutes after he had been sealed in the capsule, thirty-two hours after he had left the earth, Major Simons thumped into a South Dakota farmer's field.

A frisky wind toppled the capsule on its side and dragged it 20 feet. Simons hit the releasing switch and the aluminum dome popped open.

A farmer and his son astride horses spotted Simons and came riding across the field. The balloon rider crawled from

38

the aluminum shell, took off his helmet, and said to the approaching riders, "Hello, how are you today?"

"Howdy," replied the farmer, as he tried to keep his horse from shying as a helicopter approached and landed.

Otto Winzen, Captain Archibald, and Colonel Stapp stepped from the copter to shake Simons's hand.

5 CHAMBERS OF HORRORS

His right side shivered from the freezing cold; his left side sweated from the heat. This is how it will be sometimes in outer space. The side of the body nearest the sun will bake while the side of the body away from the sun will freeze.

The volunteer sat in a hot-cold chamber at Wright Air Development Center. Scorching-hot lights shone on the left side of his body and at the same time, on his right side, a chill wind knifed through clothing and skin to his very marrow. The temperature in the strange chamber could be changed from 50 below zero to 500 degrees above zero in four minutes.

When a spaceship begins circling beyond the atmosphere for an eventual earth landing, the side of the ship facing the sun will glow roasting hot; the side away from the sun will be freezing cold. Space scientists must find a way to protect the crew from these extremes. The hot-cold chamber is being used to help solve this problem.

Scientists are also using the chamber to study a way to precool spaceship crews. In this series of experiments they are seeking a method to cool the bodies of the crew members just before their incoming ship enters the high heat zone of our atmosphere. So far a successful precooling method has not been found, but this is just another of the many problems that must be worked out before we have safe space flight.

Air Force space scientists locked Major Arnold I. Beck in a chamber empty of oxygen. The chamber was almost an absolute vacuum. To protect himself against the lack of oxygen the major wore a pressurized MC-4 space suit and pressure helmet. Without this clothing he would have been dead in seconds.

Major Beck was on a dangerous journey into the world of outer space. He was ascending through the earth's atmosphere to a height of 198,770 feet—nearly 38 miles straight up. He actually went nowhere, but remained seated in the high-altitude chamber at Wright Development Center.

His "space flight to nowhere" took less than an hour, but Major Beck spent two hours preparing for the 198,770-foot ascent. For two hours before entering the chamber he inhaled pure oxygen to lower the nitrogen content of his blood. Too much nitrogen causes bends, the same kind of bends that are the dread of deep-sea divers.

Major Beck has made more than a hundred "flights" in

the chamber; seven were simulated journeys above 135,000 feet.

Suppose that at a make-believe 198,000 feet in the high-altitude chamber Major Beck's space suit failed, what would have happened to him? He would have passed out in twelve seconds, and if the technicians standing by outside had not got him out of the chamber in twenty seconds his brain would have suffered serious damage.

In all his high-altitude "flights" Major Beck's special clothing held up against the pressure of outer space. He was willing to risk his life to prove that the MC-4 suit was safe for space travel.

Scientists believe that the amount of oxygen in a spaceship cabin should be at least equal to that of the earth's atmosphere at 10,000 feet altitude. To find out how men perform under conditions of low oxygen a hundred subjects remained for twelve hours in an altitude chamber set at 10,000 feet.

The men were given tests designed to show what type of man is best suited to be a member of a spaceship crew. Steadiness of hands was studied. The men were told to hold a stick inside a small loop; the trick was to keep the stick from touching the loop's sides. This test showed muscle co-ordination.

The volunteers also did exercises in the chamber. They stepped on and off a low platform, and then their heart and blood responses were tested.

Their next chore was to plunge their feet into ice-cold water to see how well they could withstand the sudden

8. A pilot sits in a cockpit inside a high-altitude chamber waiting to test his reactions when oxygen is removed from the cockpit.

shock of exposing their bodies to freezing cold. Then they got on the tilt table, which raised their feet above their heads and then lowered them. The men's reactions to these tests showed physiologists who was and who was not a good risk for a space trip. Space travel demands a well-co-ordinated man.

Total darkness surrounded First Lieutenant Gilbert E. Johnson. He tried not to think about it, but he could not help it. He had but a single thought: how dark, how utterly dark it is in here.

He struggled to forget the dark, but it was always there like a solid wall of inky blackness. He tried to occupy his restless hands, but he could find nothing to do.

His eyes were useless, he could not see in the dark. Isolated in the silent cell he might have been a million miles out in the blackness of space. Instead, he was sealed in an anechoic (no echo) chamber, 15 by 7 by 7 feet, at a busy Air Force base near Dayton, Ohio. The chamber contained a chair, a table, a bed, a refrigerator, and sanitary facilities. Nowhere in the room was there the faintest light or the tiniest sound.

The minutes plodded silently by. Life in space may be like this for hour after hour, day after day. The volunteer was going to find out how long a man could stand the total absence of light. If a spaceship's power was damaged, knocking out even the emergency lights, how could the crew work? How well could they take the long darkness? If a spaceship pilot cracked under the strain and lost control of his ship it would mean death for all on board.

44

Lieutenant Johnson groped his way to the refrigerator and opened the door. No light winked on, no "click" of an opening door came to his straining ears, for light and sound were locked out of the room. He picked up a food package, and special code markings on the carton told him exactly what was in it.

He did not eat all the food in the package. He had to ration it because he did not know how long he would be in

9. In an attempt to see how long a man can endure complete isolation Lieutenant Gilbert E. Johnson spent seven days and nights in this sound-proof, light-proof chamber. The room was lighted only for the second needed to take this photograph.

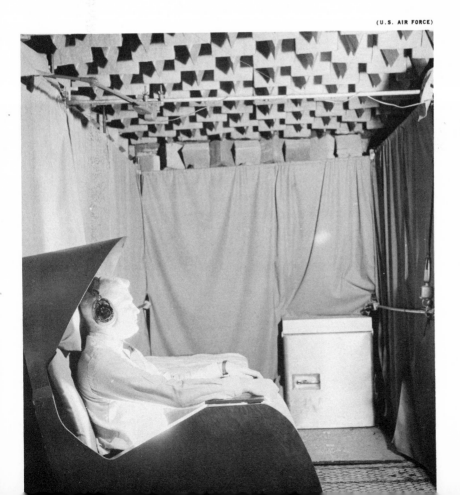

the chamber. He slept, he woke, he sat and thought about his life from boyhood to now. He touched all parts of his life in memory as the days ground by, and he just existed. He slammed his fist down on the table, but no sound came back to his ears; he was even without the companionship of earthly sounds.

The first space vehicles will carry only one man, and the volunteer was also testing a man's reaction to isolation. In time larger spaceships will carry groups of men.

After seven days and nights in the chamber the young man's nerves were at the breaking point. He pushed a special key and the alert engineers watching outside the chamber went into action. Slowly they allowed light and sound to seep into the cell. The volunteer blinked. He stared at his hands in awe. For the first time in 168 hours he could see his hands. He was free of the inky darkness. He had shown that man could live in the silent, lonesome blackness of outer space. Since then more than a hundred men have sat it out in the dark and silent chamber. By living hour after grueling hour in these chambers of horrors they have brought man closer to safe space flight.

6 HOT BOX

Blazing lights burned into him and rivulets of sweat poured from his squirming body. He knitted his brows.

"Concentrate, concentrate," he repeated over and over. "Keep control of the spaceplane."

Hour after hour pilot D. M. ("Bud") Dunafon had been baking under a battery of powerful lights seeking the answer to these questions: (1) How long and how much heat can a spacecraft pilot stand without conking out? (2) How much superheat can a pilot take without losing control of his ship? How much heat can he stand before he allows his craft to plunge back to earth a fiery coffin that will fry him to a crisp?

Space scientists know that man-carrying spaceships will glow to a red-hot 2,000 degrees upon re-entering the earth's

47

dense atmosphere. How high will the temperature climb inside the ship? Reports from the Explorer "moons" have told us that temperatures inside the satellites range from 43 to 105 degrees. This is bad for spacemen. Human beings sealed inside space suits grow miserably uncomfortable once the thermometer rises above 75 degrees.

Volunteer Bud Dunafon is helping the Human Factors and Aviation Medicine groups at Convair in San Diego, California, to unlock the heat puzzle. He undergoes the heat-fatigue tests in the cockpit of an F-102 jet aircraft. The cockpit is stationary; the only thing that moves in this experiment is the temperature, and that goes up and up.

Banks of infrared lights put the heat on Dunafon. Wires and rubber tubes connect him with a bank of recording instruments outside the shrouded cockpit. The maze of instruments carefully record the hot-box rider's body temperatures, pulse, respiration, blood pressure, heart action, and general body efficiency.

Researchers can see the volunteers through a system of mirrors. A tape recorder plays a jumble of noisy sounds into the cockpit deliberately to grate on the pilot's nerves.

As the heat mounts, the research team asks Bud Dunafon to solve complex mental problems and notes how long it takes him to answer, and how good his answers are.

One volunteer actually sat in a 1,400-degree furnace at the Minnesota Mining and Manufacturing Company, and lived. His body was protected by a suit coated with an ultrathin layer of aluminum; under the aluminum was a layer of glass-fiber quilting. Experimenters found that the alum-

48

inum reflected nine tenths of the heat, and that the glass-fiber quilting absorbed the rest. The tester felt only the heat of his own body. An insulated tube fed him air. And, although the wicker chair on which he was sitting burst into flames in seconds, the volunteer felt no ill effects.

Hurtling back into the earth's air blanket from outer space will be the most critical operation for rocketship crews. It will be squarely up to the crew to endure the mounting heat caused by air friction.

As second by second the heat grows more intense the returning astronauts must neither wilt nor falter. They must keep firm control of their emotions. Mental or physical weaknesses could mean loss of ship control and horrified ground observers would see a meteorlike flash arcing across the skies—a spaceship burning to a cinder.

Rub your hand quickly, pressing hard, back and forth across a wooden desk or table. The burning sensation you feel is friction at work. The same thing happens when a spaceship slams into the invisible layer of air that swathes our earth. As the speeding space vehicle "rubs" against the slow-moving air particles, which cannot get out of the way in time, they tear and claw at the object trying to push through. The air particles hit against the ship's cone and sides. Soon a vicious heat is generated. If this superheat is allowed to build up too long it will melt metal.

Even a comparatively slow-moving auto creates friction as it passes through our air. Metallurgists, men who study metals, say that the body of an auto is six tenths of a degree hotter when it is moving at 60 miles an hour than it is when

49

standing still. An airliner's fuselage is 16 degrees hotter at a speed of 300 miles an hour than when it rests on the runway. Imagine how much heat is generated by an object screaming through the air at 2,000 miles an hour.

Taking off and landing are usually the most dangerous periods in the flight life of an airplane and this holds true for ships of space.

High-temperature tests at UCLA (University of California at Los Angeles) have proved that generally young men can take heat better than older pilots. They are able to work longer and more efficiently at high temperatures. Volunteers were placed in a flight simulator, which is a device that looks and acts like a real airplane cockpit. The heat testers, all airplane pilots, "flew" imaginary flights. However, no matter what the pilot's age, the experiments showed that heat affected his flying know-how. The greater the heat the more mistakes he made.

Yet rocketship crews can endure extreme heat, for a while —perhaps long enough for the fast-thinking pilot to work his way out of a jam.

Through a series of experiments Dr. Konrad Buettner and his University of Washington students have found that a man wearing no clothes can withstand air as hot as boiling water (212 degrees) for almost an hour. Ordinary clothing will protect him for a minute and a half from temperatures twice as high as a 350-degree kitchen oven. Sitting in simulated airplane cockpits the students discovered that twelve minutes in air heated to 235 degrees was about all they could take. After that they made mistakes that could cause a plane to crack up.

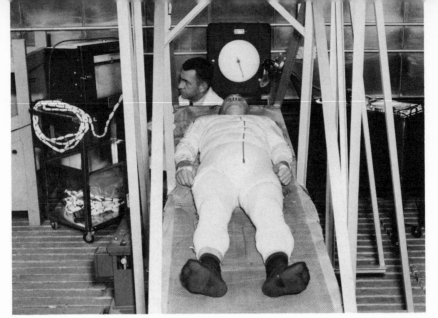

10. An Air Force volunteer is weighed before he enters the heat chamber to test his ability to withstand high temperatures.

A young man dressed for space flight walked alone into the heat chamber. An airtight Air Force crash helmet with a plexiglas window in front protected his head. A form-fitting space suit encased his body. From the tips of his toes to the top of his head not a part of him was exposed. His suit glistened as its aluminum outside covering caught the light. How well would the new-type space suit ward off heat? He was here to find out.

He eased himself into the chamber's pilot chair. Carefully he went through a final equipment checkout. He made doubly sure that his oxygen-supply tube was not snarled. The treated rubber tube would pipe vital air from outside the chamber into his suit. He inspected the many wires leading from his suit to an instrument panel on the outside of the heat chamber.

51

"All checked out," he said into the intercom inside his helmet.

"Roger," he heard a Wright Air Development Center doctor standing outside the chamber answer, "test under way."

The doctor flipped a switch and bright light flooded the chamber. Lights, hundreds of them, began glowing. From the ceiling, from the walls, from the floor, like hundreds of eyes, the lights focused upon a lone man in a space suit.

In moments the infrared lights zoomed the temperature in the chamber so high that you could have fried eggs there. The temperature soared still higher, but the safety suit's aluminum exterior bounced the heat rays away from the volunteer's flesh. The suit was a success—up to a point. It was not 100 per cent safe and no one knew that better than the man inside it. An accident to the air hose could spell trouble. A rip in the protective aluminum shield would let the sizzling heat through. Aboard a spaceship a sudden fall against a sharp projection could pierce such a suit and in seconds the astronaut would be fighting for his life.

That is why the tests must go on. New materials for safety suits that will ward off the heat generated by rocket-ships moving through the earth's atmosphere must be found. Space suits flexible enough to allow space crewmen to work yet strong enough to protect them from frying heat must first prove themselves in the heat chambers. That is why the battle against the heat barrier continues in many space labs. But that battle is slowly being won.

7 SPACE SUIT TESTERS

The three men dressed in "GUS" dived one by one into the swimming pool. GUS stands for Garment, Upper Stratosphere. The space suit wearers bobbed to the surface and swam about easily. Their suits kept them afloat.

Even if GUS is punctured it keeps its wearer's head abovewater. GUS is a success. If rocketship crews have to bail out over the ocean, GUS will save their lives.

The "Dunker" is a special suit tester. It is an airplane cockpit on wheels which run on a track leading to the edge of a deep tank of water. A man wearing a space suit climbs into the cockpit and closes the canopy. At a given signal Dunker rolls down the twin rails and plunges into the deep water. The cockpit flops over and in this upside-down position begins to sink rapidly.

Inside the cockpit the trapped pilot starts his fight to escape. He slides back the canopy and wiggles out of the topsy-turvy cockpit. With careful speed he clears the sinking cockpit, making sure he doesn't catch or rip his space suit. Using powerful arm strokes he propels himself to the surface.

His helmeted head pops free of the water. Swimming to the tank's edge he climbs out. He has chalked up another safe escape from the Dunker at the Navy's Space Training Unit at North Island, San Diego, California.

"The first few hours were okay," said the Air Force man; "after that it was like a furnace." This was the report Master Sergeant Marion L. Aydt gave scientists after he spent forty-eight hours locked in a space cabin while wearing a glove-tight space suit. During the forty-eight hours he ate baby food and drank hot tea and milk; he slept a little, but he had to do it sitting bolt upright.

Scientists gave him problems to work out to see how well man can live and work under such conditions. Asked how it felt to be sealed in the tight-fitting suit, Sergeant Aydt replied, "Pretty uncomfortable."

Could a man change into a skin-tight pressure suit fast enough to save himself if his rocketship lost its air pressure? Air Force Master Sergeant Samuel Karst and Dr. Bruno Balke found out. They stepped fully suited into a tiny pressure chamber at the Air Force's School of Aviation Medicine near San Antonio, Texas, and for ten days they slept, ate and worked inside the cramped chamber.

Dr. Balke, a physiologist, and Sergeant Karst, an aeromedical technician, lived on water, fruit juices, coffee, canned soup and baby food. Their only means of communication with the technicians outside the chamber was by intercom.

The purpose of their ten-day endurance test was to collect data which would help in selecting and training future spacemen. During the test the men studied the ways in which too much heat, lowered air pressure, and excess carbon dioxide affected their bodies.

They took a space suit apiece with them. Each day they practiced getting into the tight-fitting suits. On the fifth day a simulated emergency was staged. It duplicated a spaceship being punctured by a meteoroid. The chamber's pressure dropped to a near-vacuum. Balke and Karst had scant minutes in which to put on their suits, but they made it in time.

On the sixth day the protective canvas over the chamber was removed, allowing the sun to beat down directly on the steel cubicle. As the temperature rose inside, the men repeated their work tasks. They rode a bicycle-like gadget and tested their reflexes and co-ordination on an instrument known as a complex co-ordinator. They also worked long, exhausting mathematical problems.

Water was then sprinkled on the roof to bring the temperature down. On the seventh, eighth and ninth days the heat was allowed to build up again and the men repeated various physical and mental tasks, then checked their pulse, blood pressure and rate of breathing. Emerging from the sealed cubicle after 240 hours of isolation, the men were tired but in good health. Both had lost eight pounds.

55

How does it feel to be zipped into a moon suit? Under normal conditions the rubber and nylon suit fits snugly but comfortably. It is not until a high-flying plane or space-ship loses air pressure that the space suit proves its usefulness.

Compressed oxygen automatically inflates the rubberized tubes along the suit's arms, legs and back. This makes the suit clutch at every part of the body with an almost viselike grip. The wondrous suit actually holds the spaceman together, and he feels as though he is wearing a giant skin-tight glove. At the same time his helmet fills with compressed oxygen and forces the life-giving gas into his lungs. Air pressure inside the suit remains at a level equal to the pressure of air at 35,000 feet.

If the spaceship loses its air supply at 63,000 feet or more, he will be doubly glad he has on a space suit. At 63,000 feet human blood boils like water in a teakettle because at this altitude blood boils at 98.6 degrees, the normal temperature of the body's blood. But when the spaceman is wearing his special suit he is protected by the suit's air pressure, which equals that at 35,000 feet.

The moon suit helmet is mounted on ball bearings to permit the spaceman to turn his head easily. Space suits are made by hand and are tailored exactly to fit each pilot; flight boots are built to fit his foot. Should a crewman be forced to bail out over water his suit will float him face up until rescue comes.

Navy test pilot Commander Jack Morrissey proved that the Mark IV lightweight full-pressure high-altitude suit could be worn safely in space by testing the suit in high-

(U.S. NAVY)

11. Commander Jack Morrissey climbs into a Navy F8U Crusader jet to try out an omni-environment full-pressure suit.

flying jets. The Mark IV garment is similar to suits spacemen may wear when they walk on the moon. Two million dollars' worth of the gray-green suits, which contain 1,600 parts, are being made for the Navy by the B. F. Goodrich Company.

How does a pilot go about getting into his space suit?

First he puts on special "thermal underwear" to keep him warm. Over this he puts cotton underwear and socks. Now he sits on a chair and begins to get into the suit itself; he pulls on one leg of the suit, then the other. Next he closes the ankle zippers, puts on his boots and laces them.

Now he stands up and pulls the suit over his hips. He inserts the right and then the left arm into the garment, working the suit up over his shoulders. Reaching back over the shoulders he pulls the suit over his head.

The next step is to grasp the neck bearing with both hands and pull it up over his head. Then he lowers the suit's neck bearing straight down over his head and closes all the zippers. He buckles and tightens the chest strap, the side straps, and the rear cable straps. He needs help to tighten the rear cable straps and the flotation garment and chute harness.

Now he is ready for the gold-colored helmet. He brings the headpiece down over his head, making certain to fit his ears in the earphone cushions, and locks the suit's neck bearing to the headpiece. This also requires help. The pilot must make sure the headpiece is locked on, or it will leak.

When the pilot is in the plane cockpit or the spaceship cabin he connects the suit's oxygen hose and communications plug to outlets in the ship. The last thing he does is to zip on his gloves.

Pilots must check their suits for tears, punctures, damaged zippers, loose or broken snaps or buckles, and broken stitches. They must watch for damage to the headpiece. Every part of the garment must be in perfect condition or it may spring a fatal leak.

Suppose a rocketship lost all its air and the crew had to inflate their space suits; could they fly the ship while dressed

58

in fully inflated suits? Would the inflated suits allow the men enough freedom of movement to work the intricate controls?

Tufts University is conducting experiments to determine the best kind of space suit for this purpose. Ten men are testing suits fitted to their individual measurements. The results of the tests will help scientists design a space suit that will not cut down a man's ability to operate his spaceship when it is inflated or pressurized.

The "Moon Room" door clanks shut. Oxygen is rapidly sucked from the room until it resembles the airless moon. Inside the room a scientist lumbers about in a 50-pound moon suit, looking more like a robot than a man. He almost resembles the tin man in *The Wizard of Oz*. His chest is encased in metal, his arms are covered with accordion-pleated nylon-rubber material. This new type of protective suit may be the answer to the true, safe moon garment.

Our heavenly neighbor will prove a treacherous place for an earthling. Jagged rocks may cut the explorer's suit. Sometimes heat will burn down upon him but, worse, during the long moon night the icy cold of more than 200 degrees below zero will nip at the moon walker.

His suit must give him oxygen to breathe, heat to keep warm, cooling devices to withstand the burning sun's rays. His garment must be like armor, yet flexible enough for easy movement. To endure his moments on the moon a man must wear a suit that is a bit of earth wrapped about him.

8 MOON ON EARTH

The scientist's lungs felt as though they were on fire. He opened his mouth wide, gulping in mouthfuls of thin air; a sick dizziness made him sweat all over. The 14,250-foot altitude was proving almost more than his body could stand, yet he kept pumping the stationary bicycle.

Yesterday when he had pumped the machine at sea level down in Berkeley, California, it had been an easy task. But then a light plane whisked him 14,250 feet atop White Mountain, where the rarefied air made it an almost impossible job. It was the hardest physical labor he had ever done. Around him other scientists moved with sprightly steps. They had been at the remote mountain outpost for two to three weeks and their bodies had become accustomed to the high altitude.

Perched atop the rugged White Mountain of Central California is a high-altitude research station where scientists study the effects of lack of oxygen and cold on human beings. Set in a landscape that could have been borrowed from the moon itself, it is the highest year-round research lab in North America. The station includes three laboratories: Crooked Creek at 10,150 feet, Barcroft at 12,470 feet, and the Peak.

The White Mountain scientists have learned many secrets that man can use in space. They have found that on the first day after reaching an elevation of 12,500 feet a man can do only one-third the amount of work he could have done at sea level; by the end of a week he can do half as much as he could at sea level. Two weeks of high-altitude living makes it possible for him to accomplish 90 per cent of the work he did at sea level. After two weeks his work capacity gradually increases until it is almost the same as it was at sea level.

Scientists have also learned that living and working at extremely high altitudes strain the human body almost to the limit of its endurance. The conditions under which the White Mountain scientists live resemble those on the moon, and the experiments they are conducting will help moon explorers.

Even while building Barcroft, the White Mountain's second highest laboratory, scientists used themselves as subjects for experiments. Barcroft laboratory, 2,000 feet lower than the Peak, was constructed in 1951 by fourteen graduate students in physiology (the study of life and living organisms) plus five professors of physiology. They put

61

in hard and long hours to finish the 40-by-100 Quonset hut during the short June-to-September building season.

Working in the thin air at 12,470 feet elevation gave the scientists a feeling of mental depression, a feeling that develops in most people at high altitudes. They discovered that they did not feel like working. But they kept plugging away and finished the laboratory before winter set in. Then they began carrying their instruments to their mountain retreat.

Some of the scientists at Barcroft and at the higher Peak laboratory have been studying the effects of thin air on their breathing and their lungs. Others busy themselves with the problem of altitude sickness, while others are experimenting to determine how long they can work without rest in the high altitude.

Some of the same men who wintered atop California's White Mountain spent the winter of 1958 in the antarctic, where they kept records of the effects of frigid weather on their bodies.

Icy winds slashed snow against the young scientist's face. A chill that only antarctic weather could bring crept through twenty-three-year-old Dave Reed's winter clothing.

The mercury edged downward to 50 below. A weak summer sun glinted on the icescape, but the antarctic knows no real summer, only eternal winter. Yet because the "Great White Continent" is one of the best places on earth to study cosmic bombardment Dave Reed was braving the vicious, ripping winds and the 50 to 60 below zero temperatures to take cosmic ray observations.

How harmful will cosmic rays be to space travelers? The scientist was seeking the answer. Working under the International Geophysical Year's (IGY) Ionosphere-Cosmic Ray Program, Reed and others like him were studying the mysterious, piercing rays that pepper our world from deep in space.

Trying to unlock the secrets of space was a big part of the work of "Operation Deepfreeze." More than a hundred American scientists, together with men from other nations, studied in this cruel, vast waste of ice and treeless mountains during "Deepfreeze IV" in 1959. So rich in scientific wonders is the strange continent that in 1959 twelve countries, including the United States and Soviet Russia, agreed to make Antarctica a permanent scientific laboratory.

Ice has devoured the entire land mass of Antarctica. A crushing layer of mile-thick ice hides an area so huge that it could cover the United States and lap over the sides. Only the continent's rugged mountains keep their heads above the hungry ice.

Unknown to man for hundreds of thousands of years, shut off from surrounding continents by forbidding seas, this cold, silent waste is the last outpost before space.

Living conditions on the moon are very similar in some respects to those on the antarctic continent. That is why the South Polar region is a good proving ground for future moon explorers. In both places men must wear special protective clothing. In the land of eternal ice they must always be on guard; one tiny mistake may be the last. It will be the

63

12. Scouting helicopter lands aboard the *Northwind* off the Antarctic coast. At center is the icebreaker *Burton Island*.

same on the moon. The slightest misstep could bring death to the careless moon explorer and to the entire moon party. To the small army of scientists dug in for a 12-month Antarctic stay the bleak continent seems as remote as the moon. Winds, 200 miles per hour strong, whip at the men and swirl blinding snow cocoons about them. It is as though every inch of the 5,000,000-square-mile land hated human beings; in its worse moments Antarctica seems to fight man with a wild fury.

A region as hostile as space itself lies in wait for the un-

64

wary. Cunningly the continent covers its crevasses with a snow mantle. A hasty step and the false bridge caves in, plunging the intruder into an ice-walled canyon.

On a day in April the sun did not rise over the South Polar Plateau; for the IGY South Pole Station the long antarctic night had begun. Not until August, four months away, would the eighteen Navy men and scientists see the sun.

Snuggled under the drifting snow, and directly atop the Pole, lay the cluster of huts and burrows of the IGY South Pole Station. Inside the dwellings, built by the Navy's Seabees, men worked for science. Month after month the scientists diligently pursued their observations.

Spacemen aboard outward-bound rocketships will be crowded together just as were the South Pole scientists. Time drags and nerves grow raw when men are cooped up with the same people for months on end. Men stationed at moon outposts will someday experience the same shut-off-from-civilization feeling as these carefully picked men felt at the very bottom of our world.

A joyous shout rang out across the antarctic wastes. Sno-Cats lurched and growled toward the onlookers at Scott Station. The Fuchs scientific party was coming in from their 2,250-mile trek—the first land crossing of Antarctica.

After the greetings and the congratulations a British physiologist and an Army medical officer began to give the men physical tests to learn what the grueling journey had done to them.

Each member of the Commonwealth Transantarctic Expedition was an expert in some field of science. Throughout the hazardous trip each had made careful studies. Setting out from Shackleton Base on the Weddell Sea in November, 1958, the Britishers had pushed to the Pole, then on to Scott Station on the Ross Sea as they crossed the white continent from sea to sea.

Their first base, South Ice, lay about 250 miles inland as the crow flies, but to reach it the party's weasel, a powerful tracked vehicle, and its four Sno-Cats, had to travel 400 miles across two high mountain ranges and numerous crevasses.

Sledge-pulling huskies reconnoitered ahead of the machines. Although Sno-Cats have treads that glide across snow as lightly as a man on skis, the machines caved through many crevasse snow bridges. Luckily the heavy vehicles did not plunge so deep that they could not be hauled out of the yawning chasms by the other Sno-Cats.

Sheer, icy cliffs towered suddenly across the party's path, forcing them to skirt the obstructions. Later, stretching miles before them, lay a flat plain, laden with deep, soft snow, similar perhaps to lunar dust plains on our moon. The chugging machines found the going heavy there.

Warmer-than-usual weather began to soften the snow bridges spanning the crevasses. Nine different times the vehicles broke through and had to be pulled out. One morning the party awoke to see a heavy snow falling on their tents.

Later some of the men came down with "white-outs." White-outs occur on overcast days and are caused when light is trapped between the low-hanging clouds and the snow below. The space between snow and clouds fills in with a malted-milklike whiteness and the polar traveler's world becomes a white mass, which distorts his vision.

They had also to contend with sastrugi, the steep, wind-formed ridges of hard-packed snow which are so much a part of the antarctic landscape. The Sno-Cats pitched and slid their way over and around these obstacles which often reach a height of more than four feet.

But delays and hazards did not stop Fuchs and his companions from fulfilling their purpose of making scientific observations. A team of scientists would push ahead, set up instruments and take measurements. At ten-mile intervals the experts took core samplings which revealed the structure of the thick ice. Another group made gravity meter tests every 15 miles. And every 30 miles seismologists bored holes and set off dynamite charges. These explosions showed what lay hidden under the mile-thick ice layer. The British scientists found that the antarctic continent is not split in two, as some scientists have believed, but is one solid land mass.

When they reached the Pole Sir Edmund Hillary, conqueror of Mount Everest, strode out to meet them. After a brief stay at the polar huts Fuchs and his associates started up their Sno-Cats. Together with Hillary and his men, who had blazed a trail from the opposite side of the continent, they chugged away into the whiteness.

Ninety-nine days after leaving Shackleton depot the exhaust plumes of their vehicles were spotted by the waiting Scott Station personnel on McMurdo Sound.

The Transantarctic Expedition had won out over the

67

hostile land. These were the first men to cross the antarctic continent by land from coast to coast. They won fame and brought back a wealth of information about Antarctica and about the way men react to extreme cold and hardship.

Man was not built to withstand cold, claims scientist R. K. MacPherson; he can take heat much better. Yet cold is everywhere in outer space. It is a cold many times more frigid than that at the earth's polar regions. In space cold may reach absolute zero—a fantastic 424 degrees below.

But space experts now have a weapon to beat the cold—heated space suits.

Just as man has survived life on Antarctica, so will he survive the dangers of space travel.

9 UNDERWATER SPACESHIPS

A-uuuu-guh, a-uuuu-guh, went the submarine's dive-warn-ing klaxon horn. The helmsman's voice came loud and clear over the sub's public-address system, "Dive, dive." Crew members turned valves and the icy-cold waters of Bering Strait gushed into the ship's ballast tanks. Slowly the steel-hulled *Nautilus* slipped beneath the waves. One of the world's strangest voyages was under way.

Ninety-eight men, thirteen officers and five specialists were headed for a dangerous mission under the arctic ice. It might just as well have been a voyage into outer space, because the 116 men were sealed inside a craft not much different from a rocketship. For all practical purposes the atomic sub could be a spaceship 200,000 miles out from earth. For an atomic submarine is more like a spaceship than any other craft in the world.

69

The *Nautilus* skipper, Commander William Anderson, spoke into the sub's public-address system: "Our destination is Portland, England, via the North Pole." In this way the crew got the news which had long been kept secret: they were going to navigate across the top of the world beneath the ice pack.

At submerged depth the atomic sub started her search for a route under the ice. She had moved into Bering Strait and now was feeling her way into the Chukchi Sea. Treacherous, jagged ice lurked above; below was the bottom of the shallow Chukchi Sea. Had the crew made one serious mistake, their ship might have smashed up into the ice or down onto the ocean floor.

The little-known Chukchi Sea, ranging in depth from 105 to 170 feet, stretches for 400 miles between Alaska and Siberia. Just beyond it the Arctic Ocean basin begins. Unlike the Chukchi Sea, the arctic basin falls away to great depths which are safe for speedy submarine travel.

Commander Anderson anxiously watched the sonar

13. U.S.S. *Nautilus*, the world's first atomic submarine, pioneers a route under the polar ice cap.

(U.S. NAVY)

graphs, which showed 60-foot-long daggers of ice stabbing downward toward the *Nautilus*. The Chukchi Sea became more and more shallow. Two enemies threatened the undersea craft—the piercing ice and the sucking ocean mud.

Every man tensed at his station as the distance separating the ice pack and the ocean floor narrowed. The sonar graph pens showed danger. The pens work in conjunction with the sub's sonar and automatically draw lines on a graph upon which is sketched an outline of the *Nautilus*. Now the sonar pens moved closer to the part of the drawing representing the superstructure, or "sail." This meant the ice pack was dipping nearer the sail which contains the periscopes, the snorkle, and the radar antennae.

The attack-center TV screen grew darker. The dark screen told the men that the ice above was thickening. When the screen showed light it meant that the ice was thin, while a bright TV picture indicated clear water overhead.

The sonar graphs now showed ice pressing to within five feet of the top of the sail. It was too risky. They could not chance squeezing through.

Bitterly disappointed, Commander Anderson ordered a turnabout. This time the ice pack had beaten them, but they would try again.

The diving alarm rang as the *Nautilus* slid beneath the murky seas. Once again she pushed across the Arctic Circle for a second try at the ice pack.

Running submerged, the atomic sub prowled back and forth for two days searching for a hole in the ice but her sensitive instruments showed no opening. While running

71

deep off Point Barrow, Alaska, a series of weird noises on the sonar instruments made the sonarmen sit up sharply. The instruments reported moving objects close by. The noises turned out to be a school of walruses which swam alongside the 320-foot sub for a time probably investigating the gigantic intruder. Finally the skipper ordered *Nautilus* east toward the Barrow Sea Valley. The fathometers showed the ocean bottom dropping away, deeper, deeper. They had found an opening in the ice.

Skipper Anderson ordered the helmsman to steer dead ahead. The North Pole lay 1,094 miles away.

Two hundred feet—250—300—350—400 feet, down into the deep undersea trench went *Nautilus*. At about 400 feet her diving planes straightened and she leveled off below the roof of ice. She was in her natural element now, deep under the sea where she belongs. Ice spikes poked down 75 feet from the pack above, but they could not harm her. She was running too deep. Below her cigar-shaped hull the Barrow Sea Valley yawned deep and safe.

Her nuclear engine spun her propellers faster, keeping a steady 20-knot pace through the black depths. No motion rocked the ship; she was as still as your living room.

The crew settled into their routine. The three "pilots" steered *Nautilus* with airplane-type controls; however, most of the steering was automatic, as sensitive computers took care of guiding the sub.

Instruments similar to those that will line the bulkheads of space cruising ships crowded the bulkheads; colored lights winked; meters and dials glowed; indicator hands swept round and round. The pens on the sonar graphs drew lines, one—the upper—depicted the underside of the ice pack, the second, lower, line pictured the ocean floor, thousands of feet below and rugged as the moon's surface.

The nuclear engine purred smoothly. All was well. No fuel problems bothered the crew; the atomic reactor could keep *Nautilus* churning ahead for 60,000 miles if necessary.

But there was still need for vigilance. Time and again the watch squads examined the instruments and other equipment. A failure could bring trouble, trouble that could trap them, helpless, beneath the ice.

Air-conditioning equipment kept temperatures inside the undersea spaceship at a comfortable 72 degrees. Crewmen attended to the evaporators that gave them fresh water for showers, shaving, cooking, and for the vital steam plant.

How do crews of atomic subs, prowling the ocean depths for days and weeks, live without fresh air? Atomic undersea ships carry their own atmosphere. The air the crew breathes comes from a store of huge, sausage-shaped oxygen cylinders, which are curved to fit the contour of the sub's hull.

Though the crew breathes in oxygen from their "oxygen bank," they also expel deadly carbon dioxide. Too much carbon dioxide can suffocate a man, and that is why *Nautilus* has two carbon-dioxide removers to keep the atmosphere fresh. Called "scrubbers," the units "scrub" the carbon-dioxide laden air clean, making it fit to breathe again.

The "eyes" of the *Nautilus* take the form of several complex navigational aids, which keep the sub on the correct course and at the right depth. The navigational aids are so arranged that one double-checks the other, thus making sure no errors occur.

During the journey under the Pole thirteen sonar sets kept watch for the crew. Ten of the thirteen sonar, or echo-sounding, units, mounted on top of the sub, kept track of the underside of the ice pack. Three, mounted outside on the sub's bottom, bounced ping-pinging echoes off the ocean floor, measuring the distance between the ship and the ocean bottom.

A TV camera on top of the *Nautilus* points forward and upward. The TV screen is located in the attack center. Polar sunlight, glowing twenty-four hours a day upon the ice above, provides plenty of light for the ice-scanning TV camera.

Guiding the sub toward the Pole was a remarkable piece of equipment with the simple name of N6A. Without N6A the *Nautilus* might have become lost or crashed into unseen coasts. The crew, after watching its lights winking and see-ing its almost magical accuracy, dubbed it SFS—"Science Fiction Stuff." New and even better N6A's are now being planned to guide our future spaceships.

N6A is an inertial navigation system. It is a complex in-strument, which guided the sub to the Pole without the aid of stars or landmarks. It told the captain exactly where the sub was at any given time. The device's dead-right accuracy even had Skipper Anderson shaking his head in amazement. "I can't believe it," he repeated again and again.

Science Fiction Stuff was first used to guide the Navaho missile to target bull's-eyes. Then the system was installed aboard the *Nautilus* in highest secrecy months before the polar try.

While the many complex, delicate instruments acted as her ears and eyes, the officers and men went about the routine of running the sub. Sixty-five hours logged beneath the ice, and all was still shipshape. The crew worked at their duty stations four hours on and eight hours off. During their off time they could sleep, watch movies, read books, play cards, checkers or chess. The sub's mess compartment served as the movie theater. Thirty-eight different motion pictures were stocked aboard. Each film was shown twice a day. A juke box piped music throughout the sub.

Food for seventy-five days was stored aboard. While some of it was dehydrated foodstuff, the crew also enjoyed tasty bacon and eggs, sausage, fried chicken, spaghetti, steaks, and crisp vegetables.

During the entire trip none of the crew complained of feeling that the sub's bulkheads were closing in on them. This interested space experts because they had wondered how men would react to being sealed in cramped quarters for days on end.

Volunteers made the polar cruise. Before departing on what, for secrecy's sake, was called simply "ice operations," each crewman was asked if he wished to remain behind. Not one man wanted to stay in port.

As the sub glided through the arctic waters the crew watched as echo sounders showed the Arctic Ocean bottom. The vast ocean floor was long thought to be a great underwater plain, but it is not. Mountains and canyons unfolded beneath the sub's black shape.

75

The navigator, Lieutenant Shepherd Jenks, looked up from his plotting table. "Captain," he said, "the Pole is a thousand yards ahead."

Suddenly the juke-box music stopped and Commander Anderson's voice came over the loud-speaker system. He began the countdown. "Five—four—three—two—one. Mark! We've crossed the North Pole," he announced. "In humble gratitude to God, and in memory of our predecessors who succeeded or failed in attempts to reach this spot by land, we observe one minute's silent prayer."

The *Nautilus* headed south, with a happy crew. Two days later the TV screen glowed brightly. Clear water overhead. Up the sub surfaced to periscope depth. No ice in sight. For the first time in ninety-six hours the undersea craft broke surface.

Free of the ice the *Nautilus* sailed to Portland, England, where the crew were acclaimed heroes.

The *Nautilus* had remained submerged for ninety-six hours—four days and nights—as she churned beneath the polar ice pack. But another atomic sub, USS *Seawolf*, with a crew of 114, remained continuously submerged for sixty days during a cruise beneath the North Atlantic in 1958. *Seawolf's* skipper, Captain Richard Laning, reported that the sub had traveled 13,700 miles under the sea and that he and his crew could have stayed under "perhaps once again as long." This 60-day experimental submerged voyage proved to space scientists that man can endure long confinement.

Submariners cannot take normal exercise. They live and work in a cramped area of from 20 to 30 feet. Submarine

14. In the control room the crew keeps close watch as the *Nautilus* passes under the ice cap.

medical officers believe that sub crews should be given daily exercise by means of an electric vibrating machine.

Atomic sub crews suffer twice as much tooth decay as other sailors according to Captain W. R. Stanmeyer, chief of the Dental Research Laboratory at the New London, Connecticut, sub base. Doctors think this is the result of three things:

1. The amount of carbon dioxide in the sub's air during long undersea trips.

2. Increased noise in atomic subs.

3. Loss of periods of light and dark.

Atomic submariners also have more trouble with their gums than sailors working ashore or on other ships. The same problems may plague spaceship crews.

Navy scientists are now experimenting to see if algae can be used to remove carbon dioxide from the atmosphere in their submarines. Algae are microscopic plants which form green scum on stagnant pools. Algae "gardens" will be planted aboard subs in tests to see if the tiny plants will successfully remove carbon dioxide expelled by the crew. Algae, as does all of the plant family, live by means of the age-old photosynthesis process—taking carbon dioxide from the air and giving off oxygen in return.

Scientists hope the tiny plants will replace the harmful carbon dioxide with enough life-giving oxygen, which they themselves have made, to keep the sub crew alive. In addition the algae may be used as food because the plant contains nutritious vitamins.

Scientists have developed a new strain of alga which reproduces itself a thousand times a day. In the experiment aboard the subs a powerful light will be focused on the plant to make it grow. The algae, nearly as thick as blood, will be pumped rapidly past this stream of "artificial sunlight." If the experiments prove successful, someday long-voyaging spaceship crews may carry their own algae garden to keep them alive. Then an old nursery rhyme may well be a spaceman's theme song: "Spaceman, spaceman, quite contrary, how does your garden grow?"

Submarines are proving to be one of the best ready-made space laboratories. The *Nautilus's* trip under the polar ice pack demonstrated that men can live and work in cramped quarters. The *Seawolf's* 60-day underwater journey further proved that they can exist in a sealed vessel if they carry their own atmosphere with them.

10 SPACE "FLIGHT" RIDERS

Attached to the end of the 50-foot-long steel arm is an aluminum gondola that looks like a flying saucer. Inside the gondola is a cockpit where a pilot sits.

"Ready in the gondola," the pilot calls into his two-way radio.

"Test under way," the man in the control blister replies.

The 4,000-horsepower motor hums louder and the steel arm starts moving in a circle. Faster, faster the gondola whirls. In moments it becomes a blur to the onlookers. Another "Big C" run is under way.

Inside the cockpit of the centrifuge, as the gondola and its long arm are called, the pilot is beginning to suffer the crushing weight of G forces as his body is pressed down into the seat. His sight dims as the blood drains away from his brain.

79

"G" stands for gravity. Here on earth all of us feel the force of one G, that is, the normal pull of gravity. Three G's means three times the force of gravity. A man weighs three times as much at three G's as he does at one G. At ten G's a 185-pound man weighs 1,850 pounds. Being pressed back against the seat of a car by a sudden, jack-rabbit start gives us a fraction more than one G. Man cannot take many G's for long periods.

When a speeding plane or spaceship suddenly changes direction, G forces crush against the crew. During blast-off the sudden upthrust of speed will batter the spaceman. He will suffer the agony of too many G's.

The gondola pilot is undergoing the same kind of G forces that a spaceship pilot blasting off the earth will have to withstand. But the gondola pilot is going nowhere, just round and round on the world's fastest merry-go-round. TV and movie cameras photograph what is happening to him. Instruments record his heartbeat, breathing, blood pressure, heart waves, brain waves, and other body functions.

Exactly what will happen to a man when a spaceship is launched or re-enters the earth's atmosphere? The Big C spins to find the answer.

The giant centrifuge is housed in a 130-foot high cylinder-shaped blockhouse at the U.S. Naval Air Development Center 15 miles north of Philadelphia, at Johnsville, Pennsylvania. Other centrifuges are spinning in many parts of America, but the one at Johnsville is the largest and the fastest.

The six pilots who zoomed to record-breaking altitudes

15. A test pilot enters the gondola of the fifty-foot centrifuge at Johnsville, Pennsylvania. At upper right is the control blister.

in the experimental X-15 spaceplane first practiced their flights on the Johnsville centrifuge. They were: Scott Crossfield and Alvin White of North American Aviation (builders of the spaceplane); Joseph Walker and Neil Armstrong, National Aeronautics and Space Administration test pilots; and Air Force captains Robert White and Robert Rushworth.

A year before they flew the X-15 into the new frontier the pilots captured the feel of the spaceplane on the Big C. The interior of the centrifuge gondola was restyled to look

81

exactly like the cockpit of the X-15. Flights were made as realistic as possible. Here is an account of a typical centrifuge X-15 "flight" Scott Crossfield made.

After seeing to the final adjustments on his space suit Crossfield was lashed to the form-fitting cockpit seat. Rows of instruments stared at him from the same kind of instrument panel as that in the X-15.

He checked carefully to see that everything in the cramped cockpit was ready for the "fringe of space flight." Then he made contact by intercom with the man in the control blister. (The technician's control blister is built into the ceiling of the centrifuge chamber.)

In seconds Crossfield was whirling round and round at 174 miles per hour. The swift circling motion made his lips pull away from his gums. The crushing weight of gravity ripped at his insides. Not only did the gondola whirl in a circle, like a stone tied to a string, but it also tilted back and forth.

Crossfield felt an invisible punch in his stomach. He grunted in pain, knowing that the punch meant that his spaceplane's rocket engine had burned out. Now came the complete quiet. The ship was soaring through space, gliding soundlessly on the momentum of the burned-out rocket thrust.

The cockpit began to vibrate. Crossfield steadied his hands on the controls. He was re-entering the earth's atmosphere and experiencing the terrible buffeting the X-15 would take as it slammed back into our planet's thick air blanket. It was similar to the pounding a racing boat takes as it stutters across the water at high speed. The shak-

82

ing stopped and Crossfield eased the ship in for a landing.

The centrifuge arm slowed to a halt, and Scott Crossfield climbed out of the space trainer. He had ridden the X-15 into the fringe of space. Now he felt certain he could take the real X-15 there and back home again.

Acceleration forces are so great during blast-off that the pilot will not be able to lift his arms to guide his ship. He can move his fingers, however. So space scientists have devised finger-tip, or high-G stick, controls that the pilot works by means of tiny levers located on the armrest of the cockpit seat.

The conventional stick is in the usual place and is used in normal flight. Although the pilot is strapped into his seat he can work the armrest levers with his fingers. The X-15 has finger-tip controls, which X-15 pilots practiced with during their centrifuge rides.

The centrifuge "flights" uncovered flaws in the mechanism of the X-15. The pilots also made errors under the Big C's punishing maneuvering, and in a few cases the make-believe spaceplane "crashed," but the centrifuge's computer reported that the pilot would have survived. Sometimes the whirling volunteers took too many G's and blacked out. All six of the X-15 jockeys learned to fly the experimental spaceplane by spinning on the world's biggest centrifuge.

A special study of how man performs under G forces was undertaken at Wright Air Development Center where control boxes equipped with dials, knobs, levers and switches were installed in the enclosed cab of the center's centrifuge. Then a volunteer wearing a full-pressure space suit took a wild ride on "the wheel," as the centrifuge is sometimes called. As the great wheel spun him around his body endured the tortures of various G forces. Every time a light flashed on the control boxes he was supposed to turn it off. There were a number of different ways to turn off the light: one was by adjusting a lever; another by flipping a switch; another by turning a dial; still another by pressing a button. The time that it took the pilot to turn off the light was measured and recorded.

16. Dr. Edwin G. Vail is subjected to re-entry deceleration forces on the centrifuge. Wrist and fingertip controls are at right.

It was found that a man could turn off the light easily at low G's. At high G's it was a different story. The faster the wheel whirled the more gravity crushed down on the rider. And though he struggled with all his strength he could not work the controls. When he tried to flip the switches or turn the dials, the concentrated force of gravity pinned his arms to his sides, and he could not turn off the lights.

Space scientists are trying to whip the problem of acceleration. Sudden bursts of speed, as when rockets cut in, will pin a space rider to his control chair, and he will be helpless until the ship's acceleration period slackens.

The centrifuge has proved that a man covered with water can take more G's than a person out of water. Men wearing only shorts and a diving helmet were placed in a metal container filled with water. First the volunteer lay on his back in the container while the centrifuge gave him a whirling ride. At five to six G's pain stabbed his chest. Next he was whirled lying face down. This proved better. He could now stand ten G's for fifty-five seconds.

Five subjects were tested in thirty runs. In all runs the men could move their arms and legs freely while under water. The moment they tried to raise an arm out of the water gravity forced it back into the liquid.

However, experiments so far have shown that placing a spaceman in water has little advantage over having him wear a pressure G-suit. The trouble with water immersion is that it leaves the heart and lungs unprotected. Water holds all parts of the outer body in place during acceleration. But water does not protect the heart and lungs, for these organs are encased in air inside the body.

85

The rider pulled a lever on the "Iron Cross." The cross tilted dizzily on its eight-foot-high pole and jerked to one side. Cautiously the pilot eased forward on the lever beside his cockpit seat. The Iron Cross straightened out, "flying" on a steady course. The pilot was beginning to master the controls of the NASA research device.

This strange contraption—two steel beams in the shape of a cross mounted atop a steel pole—is another space-testing tool. The pilot "flies" it from an open cockpit at the front end of the cross. He controls the device by directing jets of compressed gas through special valve arrangements located at the end of each beam. The compressed gas, which comes from a tank on the floor, is fed to the cross through tubes.

The Iron Cross is an apparatus which acquaints a pilot with outer-spacecraft control. Spaceships cannot operate with the usual airplane rudders and ailerons which make use of the air sliding past them to control the plane. In space there is no air; there is nothing. Spaceships must be guided by rockets or jets. Pilots must practice many days on the cross to get the feel of this new kind of flight control.

The cockpit in which the volunteer was riding bounced like a yo-yo, and he eased up on the controls. The bucking slowed, then stopped.

"I've got it now," the pilot said into the intercom. "Let me try it again."

A technician threw a switch and the cockpit started another make-believe re-entry maneuver. The machine was simulating a spaceship re-entering the earth's dense atmosphere. Mounted on twin vertical tracks, the cockpit duplicates re-entry piloting problems. The contraption is located at Langley Field, Virginia, where the National Aeronautics and Space Administration is studying re-entry problems.

When an incoming spaceship hits the earth's thick air layer the pilot will feel a change in his ship's controls. This is why the volunteer experimenting on the Langley Field machine overcontrolled his "ship" and why the cockpit bucked like a wild bronco.

Now, on the second run, the pilot was prepared, and he nursed his controls carefully. Swoosh! The downward-plunging cockpit banged into the equivalent of the earth's air. "Easy, easy," he said to himself, as his hands caressed the controls. No bronco ride this time, and he eased the falling cockpit to a stop. "Got it whipped," he said. "Let's go through it one more time."

It takes many, many such runs before a pilot can master the re-entry maneuver.

The earthbound spaceship pilot's head drooped lower. Four days and nights of guiding his craft in from the moon was beginning to tell. His trained eyes scanned his crew. He saw signs that they, too, were showing the strain. One more day and they would be orbiting in for a landing on good old green earth.

The five space travelers had one more day to go, it was true, but they were not riding in a real spaceship. They were sealed in a make-believe craft at Wright Air Development Center. The Air Force wanted to know how well a space-

87

ship crew can stand being cooped up in close quarters for 120 hours straight. The space flight without moving took place in a windowless, ground-riding aircraft cabin. All the cabin's windows were covered to seal the men from the outside world.

One day at 9:00 A.M. the cabin's hatch closed upon the five Air Force volunteers. For the next 120 hours they lived, ate, and worked together. In one way they were lucky, their flight did not include the rigors of blast-off and re-entry.

The volunteers were kept busy. Whenever lights flashed on the ship's instrument panels they had to push buttons or move levers. They also became expert clock watchers— when the minute hand skipped a beat, they had to push a button. Scientists stationed at control panels outside the craft had them perform tasks which resembled those a space crew would do during an actual space flight.

Hidden cameras ground away, taking thousands of feet of film of the volunteers and their reactions to confinement. The men guided the space vehicle on its make-believe mission as long as sixteen hours at a time.

Suddenly a secretly planned emergency startled the men into action. Each crew member moved to his proper position and carried out his "under emergency" task, which was to take turns "flying" the ship.

After thirteen hours under way an *unscheduled* emergency plunged half the spacecraft into darkness. Part of the lighting system had failed. For eleven hours the crew carried on in semidarkness. Had all the lights gone out the men would have worked by flashlight. Next day repairs to the lights were made.

After 120 hours the spacemen climbed down their ship's ladder. They appeared alert and fresh, their faces showed no strain. The flight was a success.

Other volunteers will be subjected to longer simulated space flights until man learns all about the art of space travel.

11 EJECTION SEAT RIDERS

"Bail out!" The cry rang in the spacemen's ears when their incoming ship spun crazily, out of control, at 106,000 feet as it orbited in for an earth landing.

At the command "Bail out," the crew began ejecting themselves from the crippled ship. Fear rode with them as they catapulted out into the cold, black void more than 20 miles up. This was the most fearsome action they could think of, yet they had to do it. It was a matter of life or death.

Someday it may happen that way.

Spacemen will sometimes be forced to bail out of ships smashed by explosions or damaged in unforeseen accidents. Bailing out in space will be hopeless, for in space there is no air to fill the chutes, but if the ship happens to be close

90

to the earth, say 20 miles up, the crew can thank their lucky planets. From that height the parachuting men will probably make a safe landing. For years bail-out experiments have been conducted to find the safest way.

The space-suited jumper stood in the plane's open door. A chest parachute snuggled against his pressure suit. A second chute pressed against his back. At the jumpmaster's signal the parachutist leaped out the door. Six thousand feet below him rolled the Pacific Ocean.

As a member of the Air Force's 6511th Test Group (Parachute) the jumper was attempting to parachute into the ocean and live. One test jumper, Chief Warrant Officer Lambert of the Navy's Parachute Unit, has made more than 625 jumps. The Navy's Parachute Unit works with the Air Force's 6511th Test Group. The Navy's eighteen jumpers have made a total of more than 1,800 leaps for science and survival.

The airplane leveled off at 20,000 feet. Captain Hank Nielsen, standing in the craft's open door, tensed. He felt a slap on his leg and heard the jumpmaster yell, "Go!" The captain went out the door into the sky. This was "Project High-Dive."

Air Force Captain Nielsen had leaped from extreme altitudes before. He and Captain Edward Sperry once bailed out of a B-47 at 45,200 feet—more than eight miles up.

In this 20,000-foot jump Captain Nielsen was testing a new six-foot auxiliary chute. If it worked, pilots would be able to "hit the silk" at 90,000 feet. The extra chute slows

91

17. Ejection seat tester. (1) As the plane speeds at 450 m.p.h., a volunteer slides to safety out of the belly of the craft. (2) He slips clear of the plane and (3) falls earthward.

a plunging airman's fall at very high altitude. By using the special chute a pilot can delay pulling his regular chute ripcord until he falls to 10,000 feet.

When leaping with an old-style chute a pilot must free fall (fall without pulling the ripcord) until he has passed through the thin, upper air. This is dangerous because the free-falling pilot plunges earthward at bulletlike speed. His body spins so violently that he may black out and plunge to his death. Finally, when he does pull the ripcord his swift descent can tear the chute canopy into worthless shreds. With the parachute useless, he plummets straight to the ground.

Captain Nielsen and the other test parachutists first leaped the new chute from 20,000 feet, then from 30,000. Later they will jump from 60,000 and lastly from 90,000 feet. The 60,000- and 90,000-foot jumps are to be made from balloon gondolas.

At exactly 76,400 feet Air Force Captain J. W. Kittinger stepped out of the opening in the gondola and began the longest parachute jump in history (as of November 1959). At that height the temperature of the thin air was 104 degrees below zero. Joseph Kittinger was testing bailout and recovery equipment for spacemen. Encased in a partly pressurized suit, he plunged 12 miles in a free-fall drop that took but 2 minutes and 58 seconds. He tumbled from 76,400 to 12,000 feet, and reached a speed of 450 miles-per-hour before his twenty-eight-foot chute opened as scheduled. He drifted down to a safe landing on the New Mexico desert.

Kittinger, who knows balloons well, had ascended to the more than 14-mile-high altitude in an open gondola suspended beneath a plastic balloon. Throughout the long plunge he took readings on the many instruments strapped to his body and also recorded his thoughts and feelings on tape.

Captain Vincent Mazza fought to relax his body and struggled to remain calm. Each second he counted to himself seemed a minute as he sat in a specially made chair at the bottom of the twin rails of the ejection simulator which stretched 100 feet up the side of the test-building wall.

How fast can a man be shot out of a speeding plane and remain unharmed? How should a pilot be strapped to his cockpit chair? What type helmet and clothing will best save his life? These were only a few of the many questions the volunteer was helping to answer.

He stared straight ahead. His fingers gripped the chair arms until his knuckles glistened white. Suddenly his body jerked upward, but his stomach seemed to remain rooted to the spot. He and the chair were taking a swift ride up the rails.

In seconds his body thudded to an abrupt stop close to the building's ceiling. Another ejection-seat ride was over. Slowly the volunteer and his chair were lowered down the 100-foot-high rails to the floor. Air Force technicians unbuckled him. Medics took him to a nearby room and began testing his body reactions—his heart, blood pressure, breathing, reflexes.

Tomorrow Captain Mazza would ride the ejection device again. Only tomorrow they would increase the speed. Then on the following day the medics would try a different way of strapping him to the chair. The day after that a new-type chair would be tested.

A safe way of ejecting pilots underwater has been found by the British Navy. Should a pilot be forced to ride his plane into the sea he can still escape, thanks to this new life-saving method. To perfect the method, test pilots were ejected from a submerged mock-up of an aircraft cockpit.

"The procedure is violent," states the British Institute of Aviation Medicine, "but safe." By pushing the eject button the pilot rockets out of his sunken cockpit and slams into a solid wall of water. A shield on his helmet covers his face and his pressure G-suit protects his body as he bobs to the surface unhurt.

Here is what would happen if a pilot was forced to eject himself from the X-15, now being used to probe the fringe of space. If the high-flying craft should start to rattle to pieces at, say, 100 miles above the earth, the pilot would first bring the ship down to lower altitudes. Lowering the altitude gives the aircraft time to slow down from its great speed of 4,000 miles per hour. Not until he had plunged to 20 or 30 miles above the ground would the pilot flick the escape switch. Then automatic timers would cause the X-15's canopy to fall away and a rocket charge would shoot both seat and pilot up and out of the disintegrating ship. Flaps would pop out of the seat to halt any tumbling, and to slow the fall; the braces strapping the pilot to his seat would be released automatically.

A second rocket blast would shatter the air, freeing the falling pilot from the seat. The chute, which opens even if the pilot is unconscious, would blossom forth. The pilot, who only minutes ago wrestled a craft that was tearing itself apart in space, now drifts down to a safe landing.

The pilot of a doomed jet plane can now be shot to safety in two seconds. After ten years of experimenting Republic Aviation Corporation has designed a safe escape capsule for supersonic jets, which also solves many of the problems encountered in bailing out of space vehicles. The device is a combination seat and escape cocoon. If a supersonic jet plane gets into trouble while flying at four times the speed of sound, the pilot can save his life by pulling the ejection actuator handle of the escape capsule.

In split-second succession his feet and legs are automatically pulled back into ejection position. His shoulder and body harness is locked; his crash helmet is clasped to prevent it from twisting and his body is harnessed snugly to the seat to prevent injury to his spinal column.

At the same time the bottom of the seat rises while special sliding doors and top close over the pilot to form a lifesaving cocoon. Off goes the canopy of the cockpit. Two rocket charges catapult the snugly enclosed pilot out of his damaged ship at a speed of 65 to 70 feet per second. The entire operation takes place in two short seconds. A parachute unfurls to carry the pilot to a safe landing. The capsule floats if it happens to land in water.

This safety system can save a pilot's life when his craft is at 100,000 feet and traveling at four times the speed of sound. It is also effective at extremely low altitudes and slow speeds. At low altitudes, where the regular chute would not have time to pop open, a ballistic chute is instantly and forcibly opened. Ballistic chutes are operated by means of an artillery-type shell which explodes, forcing the chute open.

Low-altitude escape systems are now needed to cope with take-off emergencies of VTOL (vertical take-off and landing) aircraft. Space vehicles that abort on the launching pad or fail during their landing patterns also will need a low-altitude escape system.

Most space scientists believe that the answer to safe rocketship escape in the fringe areas of space and in the lower zones of the atmosphere is by capsule escape. This is how a capsule escape would take place: part of the spaceship with the crew snugly inside would break away from the damaged section. After a fall through the ultrathin air a metal chute would pop open, bringing the capsule and its human cargo to the ground. The capsule would carry its own oxygen supply and be buoyant so that it would float if it landed in the ocean.

As they drifted earthward the rocketmen could radio their plight over the escape device's built-in radio. Rescue craft would quickly locate the men by picking up the radio calls and following them to the capsule. Spaceships may also be equipped with special space "lifeboats."

Spacemen will have to practice capsule escape to be ready for emergencies. Ejection-seat riders have pioneered the best way of positioning themselves to withstand the violent shock of breaking away from the crippled rocketship. They have proved what are the best and safest kinds of helmets and pressure suits and have shown that a man can escape from a craft speeding as fast as a bullet.

12   TEST PILOTS

Test pilot Bill Bridgeman adjusted his crash helmet, checked his G-suit, and ran through an instrument check on the sleek experimental jet. The plane had been tested in wind tunnels and in straight flight but this was the shakedown, the real test flight.

When the pilot got the go-ahead from the tower he gunned the jet's powerful engine into a whirlwind take-off. In moments he had pushed her to 75,000 feet, then he rolled her over into a dive.

Would the flying blowtorch take it? Last week his buddy had tested a new ship. The aircraft was supposed to be O.K., but when the plane went into a dive it became a flying coffin and spun his friend into the ground.

Bridgeman put the memory of it out of his mind and

pushed the stick farther forward. Eyes glued to the altimeter he watched the needle swing to 30,000 feet, 25,000, 20,000—down, down—15,000—10,000. The plane screamed as it dived earthward. He hauled back on the stick. The plane responded and started to come out of its dive.

Now everything began growing fuzzy. The instrument dials grew dim before his straining eyes. As he pulled out of the dive he was caught in the powerful force of gravity. His blood was being sucked from his brain by the abrupt change in direction. He tried to stop his senses from reeling. All-powerful gravity crushed down on pilot and jet; heavier, heavier, gravity's invisible force pushed down upon him. He could feel himself about to black out.

He realized that if any flaws existed in the plane this pullout would discover them. The more flaws he found the less chance there would be of another pilot's crashing to death in a similar ship.

Slowly, painfully he leveled the jet off into easy, straight flight. Bit by bit Bridgeman came back from his near-blackout. A sigh of relief escaped him; the ship had responded well to the pull-out, it had passed the test. Throughout the flight he had kept a rundown of the jet's actions on a tape recorder for the plane's designers.

He let down the landing gear and came on in for a three-point landing. To the group of smiling aeronautical engineers at the hangar the test pilot said, "A few changes and she'll be O.K. I brought her back, didn't I?"

Today test pilot Bill Bridgeman put an ultranew jet through its paces. Tomorrow he may "wring out" a spaceplane.

George F. Smith is a test pilot who has escaped death many times—once by only two seconds. This is his story:

Smith taxied the F-100A Super Sabre to the end of the runway; he made his cockpit and instrument checks. Everything seemed right. But hold it! The stick was a bit stiff when he moved it. He waggled it, carefully watching the hydraulic pressure. The instruments read normal. There was nothing to worry about, so he made contact with the tower for take-off.

He was swishing along at 35,000 feet above the Pacific Ocean when the plane suddenly started nosing over all by itself. George began trimming the ship. The control stick wouldn't move. He tugged at it, but he couldn't budge it.

Now in a dive, the Super Sabre picked up speed. George called the North American Aviation Company's radio station XRT. "I'm having hydraulic trouble—a frozen stick," he said. The jet screeched oceanward at an 80-degree angle. Contrails from the plane showed test pilot Joe Kinkella, flying nearby, that Smith's ship was heading for the ocean. "George, bail out!" yelled Kinkella over his radio.

George knew that he had to eject himself from the Sabre jet. He was diving straight into the ocean. He made a last call to station XRT: "Controls locked. I'm going straight in."

Quickly he made ready to eject. He opened the plane's speed brake and jerked the visor of his helmet over his eyes. His right hand yanked up on the seat's armrest, automatically sending the cockpit canopy flying off and away.

A loud blast like an explosion roared in his ears. It was the sound of air rushing past his open cockpit at more than 700

101

miles an hour. He didn't remember pulling the ejection trigger. The last thing George recalled was seeing the Mach meter reading 1.05—five days later he woke up in a hospital.

This is what happened to the pilot between the time he was thrown out of his ship and the time he landed in the hospital. The instant his body was tossed from the plane it smacked a "stone wall" of supersonic air which knocked him out. Engineers later estimated that the jet had dived to within 6,500 feet of the ocean before Smith bailed out. If he had waited two seconds longer his parachute would not have had time to open.

Lady Luck watched over George Smith that day. When his parachute eased him into the Pacific he was still unconscious and could not inflate his life vest. The day was almost windless but at that moment a breeze puffed enough air into the canopy of the chute partially to fill it. This kept Smith's face out of the water for about fifty seconds—and fifty seconds was time enough for the fishing boat *Balabes* to reach the floating pilot.

Luck also played her part in bringing the *Balabes* into the area. Most of the other fishing vessels had already gone back to Newport harbor, south of Los Angeles, when a roar like that of an exploding shell shook the little boat and a geyser of water foamed upward from the sea some 200 yards behind the craft.

Fifteen-year-old Bob Simon, aboard the *Balabes* with his father and the craft's owner, Art Berkell, thought their engine had exploded.

Someone shouted: "We're in a Navy gun range! Let's get out of here!"

102

Then it was that Bob saw Smith sprawled on the waves. The *Balabes* turned around and headed for the pilot.

Joe Kinkella zoomed down in his F-100. He radioed for help to station XRT and to test pilot Frank Smith (no relation to George) who was flying nearby.

Bob Simon and his two companions struggled to lift Smith from the waters. The pilot was a sight Bob will never forget. His shoes and socks had disappeared, his clothes were cut to ribbons; his helmet and oxygen mask had been torn off and blood flowed from cuts on his forehead, chin and feet.

At last they got the injured man aboard and raced for Newport harbor. Soon they were met by a group of Coast Guard auxiliary cruisers which had been practicing rescue operations in the vicinity. On seeing the parachute drifting oceanward, the cruisers had sped toward the scene. Because the Coast Guard craft was the faster boat George's body was quickly transferred from the *Balabes*. The Coast Guard cruiser radioed ahead for an ambulance and doctors to be at dockside. At first the hospital doctors were afraid they could not save the pilot. They had never before treated a man knocked unconscious by a blast of supersonic air. The Air Force immediately rushed doctors from its Department of Aviation Medicine to Newport Beach. The Air Force doctors came from bases across America to care for the man who had been ejected from a jet traveling more than 700 miles per hour. No one in the entire medical profession had ever treated a man who had been shot from a plane at such a high rate of speed. One of the Air Force specialists was Dr. John Stapp, the rocket-sled rider.

When George Smith finally came to after five days he heard someone reading children's letters to him. A group of fourth- and fifth-graders from Aliso Elementary School in South Laguna Beach, California, had written to the injured pilot because George's plane had smashed into the water not too far from their school. The speeding plane's shock wave had even rattled the school's windows in a sonic boom. Their teacher, Mrs. Pearl Phillipson, gave them an assignment to write to the hospitalized pilot to cheer him up and wish him a speedy recovery. A nurse was reading their letters aloud when he awoke. George Smith did not leave the hospital until six months later. He had weighed 215 pounds when he took the jet up for the test flight; he dropped to 150 pounds before he recovered.

By his grueling experience George Smith saved the lives of many other fliers. As the direct result of his nearly fatal ejection a better helmet was fashioned and a new, safer ejection seat also was devised.

Test pilot George Smith, the first man to survive a supersonic bail-out, is again test-flying jets.

At 34,000 feet test pilot Lieutenant Colonel Marion Carl dropped the Skyrocket away from the "mother ship." The Marine Corps pilot had traveled to this height in a rocket plane in the bomb bay of a B-29. Now he and his experimental plane were strictly on their own. Colonel Carl gunned his rockets to full power. The Skyrocket slashed upward steeply: 40,000 feet, 60,000, 75,000, the ship climbed at a speed of 1,200 miles an hour. Even when its rocket fuel was spent the plane continued to charge into the fringe of space.

18. Looking like a man from Mars, Marion Carl sits in the cockpit of the Navy Skyrocket in which he reached an altitude
of more than 80,000 feet.

At 83,000 feet—more than 15 miles high—the Skyrocket's momentum slowed and the pilot pointed the craft's
needle nose earthward. Edwards Air Force Base loomed up
big and welcome. He banked and brought the Skyrocket
zipping across the hard-packed runway at 150 miles an hour;
he braked the plane to a halt and stepped onto solid ground.
After a flight to the fringe of space Colonel Carl was back
on earth again.

In 1953, 83,000 feet was a record. That record has since

been broken many times. In 1959 an F-104 Starfighter took off from the ground and soared to 103,395 feet—about 17 air miles straight up. In a few years a rocket-boosted glider will be piloted to 240,000 feet or more. Dyna-Soar will be its name. In "Project Dyna-Soar" space scientists hope to send a test pilot on one or more 90-minute flights around the world at heights that will take him to the very edge of the atmosphere.

Perched atop a 75-foot Titan missile Dyna-Soar will be blasted to an altitude of 80 miles; at that point the glider will part company with the missile and continue on its sweep

19. An Air Force test pilot stands next to an F-104 Starfighter, the first fighter equipped with a downward ejection seat.

around the world. After making the required earth-girdling sweeps the pilot will gently bring Dyna-Soar into its hypersonic glide. The pilot will begin dipping back down through the atmosphere into denser air. To ease the speedy space glider back to a safe landing the pilot will have to slip his ship in and out of the earth's air blanket. This action will slow the ship and also keep it from burning up as it enters the thick atmosphere.

Each time the coated molybdenum alloy skin of the glider gets too hot the pilot will ease the vehicle's nose up and soar back into cooler regions of thin air. He will continue this action until the ship has slowed down enough to permit safe entry through the earth's air cocoon.

Dyna-Soar pilots will face many problems. One is overheating as the space glider slashes back into earth's atmosphere. Another is pilot control; yet another—a constant space fear—is lack of air should the cockpit spring a leak. Last, and probably the worst, will be the battle with high G (gravity) forces and weightlessness.

Therefore, before Dyna-Soar can glide a man around the world its pilots must prepare well for the trip. Test pilots are flying high and fast in our speediest jets. They are whirling round and round in big centrifuges. They are enduring simulated flights to the edge of the atmosphere.

When they have finished practicing the pilots will begin flying the space glider. The flights will be short at first. "We'll learn to crawl before we walk," said one project scientist, "and when the time comes we'll be ready."

13   FLIGHT OF THE X-15

At 38,000 feet the experimental spaceplane suspended beneath the right wing of its B-52 "mother ship" dropped free. For the first time the X-15 was flying on its own. Test pilot Scott Crossfield guided the multimillion-dollar ship into a lazy S curve downward toward Rogers Dry Lake runway in California's Mojave Desert. On this, its first flight, the rocket plane was being released from 38,000 feet in a "dry" (without fuel) drop to give Crossfield a chance to test the controls of the 50-foot-long ship. As he piloted the jet-black spaceplane over the gigantic landing field Crossfield jubilantly radioed ground stations. "Everything is working perfectly, I wish I could do a barrel roll on the way in."

Aeronautical experts had said that landing the powerless, 7-ton X-15 would be "like driving a racing car toward a brick wall at 100 miles an hour, slamming on the brakes, and stopping two feet from the wall." Five minutes and ten seconds after dropping from the pylon beneath the B-52's right wing Crossfield brought the craft in for a flawless landing.

For the X-15 this dry flight was another step toward the fringe of space. Four times earlier Crossfield, test pilot for North American Aviation, had ridden the ship into the skies and back while it was fastened beneath the B-52's wing. This was the first time he had dropped free in an attempt to pilot the ship to a landing. Many more flights, powerless and with rocket power, are to follow before X-15 will be asked to perform its real mission—to probe space 125 to 150 miles above the earth.

When after a series of such test flights the X-15 is proved airworthy it will be turned over to the National Aeronautics and Space Agency and to the Air Force for other flights and finally for an all-out assault on the fringe of space. On the final series of space-probing flights, the craft is to be dropped from its mother ship at 38,000 feet for a full rocket-power thrust to near space. The half-plane, half-spacecraft was built under a joint Air Force, Navy and NASA program. Three X-15's have been made by North American Aviation. After Crossfield has taken the first ship through its rigorous tests to the satisfaction of NASA he will begin the same tests on the second X-15 and so on.

To gain spacecraft know-how NASA and Air Force test pilots must fly the jet-black, stubby-winged ship many times. During more than a year's training they have already endured hundreds of grueling tests to qualify as pilots for

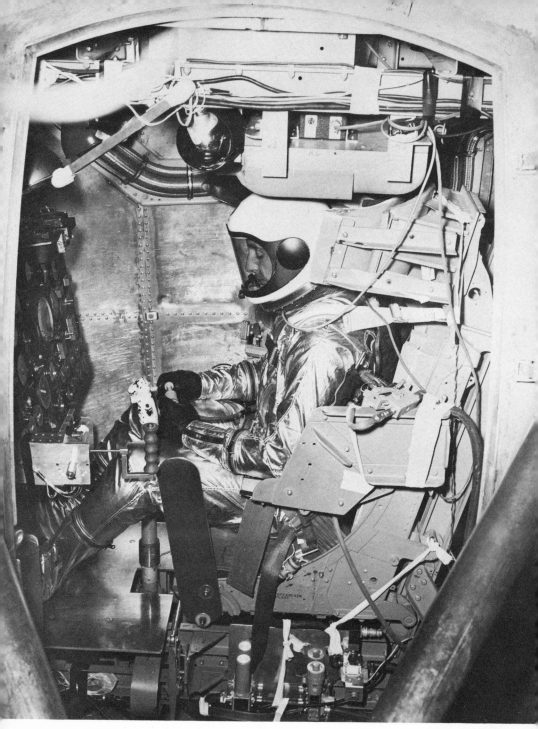

20. Scott Crossfield studies the controls of the X-15 in a mockup
of the rocket plane built into the Navy's giant centrifuge.

the superspeed craft. They have made hundreds of "flights" in a simulator of the X-15 to learn how to fly the real ship.

On his "dry" flight Crossfield was strapped to a cockpit seat which was molded to fit his body. A helmet with a plexiglas face piece covered his head, a glistening white, hand-tailored pressure suit encased his body. The suit, like the cockpit, was insulated against the terrible heat he will encounter on later, powered flights as the craft zooms through the atmosphere.

Three different kinds of control systems are built into the X-15's tiny cockpit: the first is a conventional "stick"; the second a small wrist-operated stick. The sticks are used when the craft is flown like an airplane. The third system, called ballistic control, is another type of wrist stick that controls the spaceplane's small rocket engines, located in the nose and wingtips. The rocket engines will be used as soon as the X-15 reaches the region of space.

Once the experimental ship blasts up and beyond the earth's air blanket the cleaver-shaped rudder is useless. It is then that the pilot will put the ship on ballistic control. Inconel-X, a supermetal, keeps the rocket plane from being burned to a cinder. Beneath this tough hide of nickel alloy is a layer of titanium and then a layer of stainless steel. A jet-black, special silicone paint, which can take temperatures of more than 1,000 degrees for short periods, covers the craft's exterior.

On mountaintops across Utah, Nevada, and California the "Searchers" will swing into action to watch X-15 on its many powered flights. Radar antennae will move unceasingly back and forth scanning the sky as X-15 flashes overhead on its high journey. Every second of flight will be tracked by radar and telemetry equipment. On the high flights the plane's route will cover 485 miles from Wendover, Utah, to Edwards Air Force Base, California. The X-15's speed, its temperature, the stresses its fuselage and wings undergo, and the pilot's reactions—all this vital information will be flashed to earth-bound scientists by the 1,300 pounds of instruments packed into the ship.

Information learned from pilots riding the big Johnsville centrifuge, plus other data, has told scientists that this is what will happen on a typical X-15 high flight. After dropping free from the pylon under the B-52's wing at 38,000 feet the pilot will push a button "lighting off" the rocket engine. A searing, swirling blast of rocket force equal to 500,000 horsepower will hurtle the craft upward at speeds that will reach 4,000 miles per hour. The pilot will feel himself being squeezed downward in the cockpit seat from the surge of the ship's zooming to the edge of space.

The ship will be under rocket power for about six minutes during which time it will rocket to a height of 80 to 90 miles. At this elevation the pilot will find the roar of the rocket engine growing fuzzy in his ears and then he will hear no noise at all, for he will be whizzing through air too thin to carry sound waves. He will know the silence of space.

At 150 miles he will have reached the top of his climb. Now weightlessness will grip him for about five minutes as the X-15 arcs over for the long trip down. The pilot will be on ballistic control. Should the instruments on his instrument panel tell him he is slashing downward at too steep an angle he will push the tiny control stick and small hydrogen peroxide rockets under the ship's nose will spurt to life, causing the X-15's nose to lift slightly.

21. Needle nose and stub wings identify the X-15, a research rocket plane, whose surface is covered by a special heat-resistant nickel-steel alloy.

Scientists have computed by testing small models of the X-15 in wind tunnels that re-entering the atmosphere will make the ship shake and bob up and down. It will be the pilot's ticklish job to ease his ship gradually into the thick air blanket. If he knifes too steeply into the earth's atmosphere, air friction will melt his craft. Even so the nose and

113

forward wing edges of the ship will glow red hot as X-15 bores down through the "thermal thicket." Protective insulation, plus the cabin's refrigeration system, will keep the pilot from passing out due to excessive heat. Should X-15 begin melting, the pilot has been trained to hit the escape lever which will blast him and the cockpit seat clear of the ship. A strong parachute will then float him down to a safe landing.

Plans are to have the pilot go on regular stick control at about 75,000 feet. Little by little the superplane will stop vibrating as it plunges deeper into the sea of air surrounding the earth.

Landing will be a precise job because the pilot will be coming in with zero power and at fast speeds. Flying smoothly he will slash above California's Death Valley. At 15,200 feet he will begin the no-power landing pattern, dropping to 8,700 feet, then going into a turn. He will make his final turn at 5,800 and then flare out at 3,200.

Out of the fuselage will pop struts with steel landing skids. The ship's nose wheel will move into down position. The X-15 will slow to 284 miles per hour. The pilot will line her up with the long landing strip and swish in. Nose wheel and skids will hit the concrete runway as the ship sits down at 280 miles per hour. Smoke will pour from the skids as the X-15 slides almost a mile to a final halt from its flight to the fringe of space and return in just eighteen minutes.

Even after making several successful high flights the X-15 will continue to rocket aloft, for scientists know that the unique spaceplane will bring back the answers to many space-flight problems.

14   PROJECT MERCURY

Space scientists have long known that before a man can go to the moon and the planets he must take short practice flights into space. They know that the best way to do this will be to put a man in a space vehicle and send him on an earth-circling flight that will take him into the space regions surrounding our globe. In this way both the man and the space machine will be tested.

This is why Project Mercury was planned. The project, under the direction of the National Aeronautics and Space Administration's Space Task Group, plans to blast a man into orbital flight in a specially designed space capsule. The man will make one or more swings around the globe at a height of from 125 to 150 miles and then land safely back on earth. In later flights the man-carrying capsule may circle the world as many as eighteen times. Each loop around our planet will take about ninety minutes. The capsule is to be blasted into space from atop the mighty Atlas missile.

On his blast into nearby space the volunteer will feel himself zooming up and out through the atmosphere, and during his return for a landing will undergo the sensation of coming back through the heat barrier as he re-enters the earth's air blanket.

But first a vehicle that can safely carry a man into space and back would have to be designed and built. NASA asked American aircraft companies to design such a craft. Twelve companies put their designers to work on the problem. The vehicle design brought forth by McDonnell Aircraft Corporation of St. Louis won NASA's approval as the best for the job. McDonnell was awarded a $15,000,000 contract to build three space capsules.

The Mercury capsules are cone shaped, measure about 6½ feet across and weigh 2,400 pounds. Crammed inside the tiny cabin are instruments and equipment. A contour couch cradles the pilot. Two parachutes, a main chute and an emergency one, will be packed inside the vehicle. The capsule will be constructed of tough metal to withstand speeds of 18,000 miles per hour and the searing heat of re-entry. Retro rockets built into the craft will be able to slow it up during re-entry to prevent it from burning to a cinder. It will float in case of a water landing.

There is an escape rocket at the extreme front end of the capsule in case the Atlas launching missile fails to clear the launching pad. Should the Atlas prove faulty, the Mercury pilot will push a button to trigger the escape rocket and

116

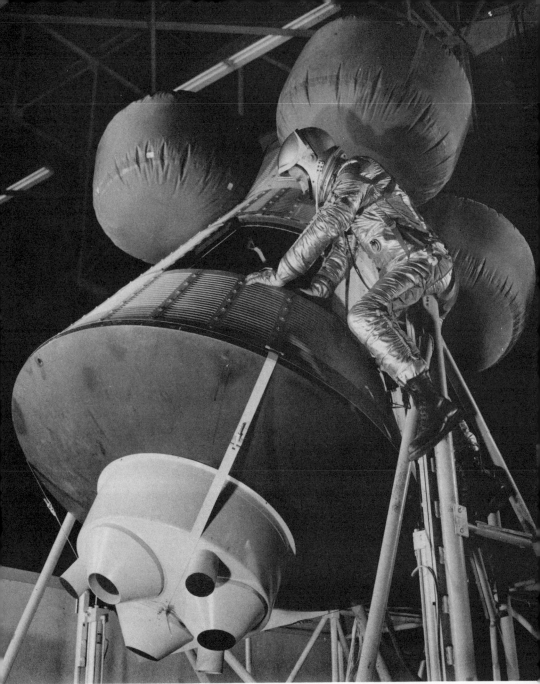

22. A pilot prepares to climb through the entrance hatch of the Project Mercury manned satellite. The retro-rockets can be seen at lower left. Flotation bags, which pop out to give the capsule buoyancy in water, are shown inflated here.

blast the capsule clear of the Atlas, sending the ship zooming half a mile up and off to one side. The chute will open and the capsule float safely to earth.

At the same time that aeronautical engineers were designing a capsule to circle the earth the search began for a man to ride the space vehicle. Because military test pilots face many conditions similar to those in space flight, NASA sought volunteers from the air services. After a careful study of the records of United States military jet pilots 110 names were picked. To be listed among the 110 a pilot must have been graduated from a university or college with a degree in engineering or physical science. He must also have been graduated from a military test pilot school and have amassed 1,500 hours flying time. He must be under forty years of age and stand five feet eleven inches high, or less.

The 110 names were quickly pared to 32, and finally, after the most rigorous physical and mental tests, seven men remained. The seven astronauts, as NASA calls them, are: Lieutenant Malcolm Scott Carpenter, United States Navy; Captain Leroy Gordon Cooper, Jr., Air Force; Lieutenant Colonel John Hershel Glenn, Jr., Marine Corps; Captain Virgil Ivan Grissom, Air Force; Lieutenant Commander Walter Marty Schirra, Jr., Navy; Lieutenant Commander Alan Bartlett Shepard, Jr., Navy; and Captain Donald Kent Slayton, Air Force.

Just before blast-off time for the first orbital flight one of the seven will be chosen to crawl inside the tiny capsule attached to the nose of an Atlas. He will close the hatch behind him and wait to be blasted into orbit. During the extensive series of Mercury flights all seven men will eventually be given a chance to ride the vehicle around the world.

From that day in April, 1959, when they were picked for the man-in-space project the seven astronauts started training for their orbital flights. They were taken aloft in a huge Air Force C-130 transport plane for training in weightlessness flying. They went skin-diving in the Atlantic Ocean to keep them in physical shape and to practice remaining oriented during the weightlessness part of their orbital trip. The astronauts learned to pilot the capsule during the time it would be weightless by "flying" a simulator of the craft. For three days they ate a diet of applesauce, beef cubes, and orange juice—the very food they will eat before and during their flight. They have learned how to eat from squeeze bottles so that they will be prepared for the weightless state of their flight.

The volunteers rode the Navy's centrifuge at Johnsville, Pennsylvania. They were put in hot chambers to see how much they would perspire when placed in the capsule. Dressed in space suits, they entered a pressure chamber and were sent to simulated heights of 100,000 feet. In dark, soundproof isolation chambers the seven have undergone the sensation of traveling through black, silent space. In the classrooms the astronauts have been studying astronomy, meteorology, astronautics, geography and missile operations, to name only a few subjects.

They have been measured and fitted for pressure suits that cost $3,750 each and have been fitted for their foam-rubber couch, which is to be made to their exact measure-

119

ments. Placed in the capsule, the couch will protect the space rider from G forces.

The astronauts will help to develop the space vehicle. Each volunteer has been assigned a special phase of the project. Lieutenant Malcolm Carpenter is responsible for communications and navigational aids; Captain Leroy Cooper for the Redstone booster to be used in the first test flights; Lieutenant Colonel John Glenn for crew space layout; Captain Virgil Grisson for the automatic and manual attitude-control system; Lieutenant Commander Walter Schirra for the life-support system; Commander Alan Shepard for range, tracking and recovery operations; Captain Donald Slayton for the Atlas booster.

As soon as the Mercury capsules are completed the astronauts will begin to operate the real vehicle. The volunteers will study the capsule's equipment, learning to test and maintain all of its complicated systems.

While the men have been undergoing tough physical and mental workouts various large and small models of the capsule have been tested to make certain the actual craft will perform to perfection. Behavior of the capsule during flight is being studied at three different NASA wind tunnels with models of the cone-shaped ship. Man-made winds up to 13,000 miles per hour scream past the stationary models showing space engineers how much heat the capsule can absorb and how it will react during all phases of flight.

How is the space vehicle to be recovered after it slices back into the atmosphere? How reliable are the capsule's two chutes? How hard will the man-carrying vehicle smack the ground or, in an ocean landing, the water? To find the answers scientists of NASA's Langley Pilotless Aircraft Research and Flight Research divisions in Virginia have been air-dropping full-scale models of the capsule. The models are dropped from a giant C-130 Hercules transport plane. Two chase aircraft following close by photograph the capsule while it plunges earthward, is brought up short by the metal parachute snapping open, and hits the ground or the Atlantic Ocean testing area. A helicopter picks up the dropped model. Both ground and water drops are studied.

Mercury's first rocket-boosted flights are to be without passengers. A Redstone missile will blast the empty craft from a Cape Canaveral, Florida, launching pad to a point 100 miles out in the Atlantic Ocean. A ship standing by will retrieve the space capsule from the water.

Monkeys are to be the vehicle's first passengers, riding the speedy capsule 100 miles down the Atlantic Missile Range. Two monkeys, Able and Baker, that in 1959 rode a missile nose cone down the range and were plucked from the sea by a standby ship, were an early part of Project Mercury.

Only after many experimental flights with monkeys have proved the capsule safe will the seven astronauts be permitted to ride the craft down the range. One by one the seven volunteers will then be blasted about 100 miles into the sky and about 130 miles down the Atlantic Missile Range. Step by step NASA's Space Task Group will feel its way along the upward path to space.

The seven astronauts agree that when the time comes riding the 18,000-miles-per-hour capsule around the world will be no more dangerous than test-flying a new-type jet fighter aircraft.

Only after exhaustive tests of both the astronauts and their capsule have proved successful will one of the seven volunteeers blast skyward on a history-making ride to the edge of space.

15 BLAST OFF TO THE MOON

This chapter describes an imaginary flight to the moon by rocketship. This is the way it may happen someday.

"Beginning countdown," the pilot's voice boomed over the spaceship's loud-speaker system. Every crew member tensed at his blast-off station. The eight-man crew had trained for many years for this moment—"Project Moon Walk."

The gleaming-white rocketship stood poised on its launching pad. The G-suited men inside were to be the first to blast off to the moon. Their mission was to land on the moon, explore a portion of its surface, and then return to earth. Their ship, the XX-1, measured 17 feet wide and 65 feet long. To enable it to land back on earth a wedge-shaped wing flared from nose cone to rocket nozzles.

123

The pilot picked up the blockhouse countdown through his earphones and repeated the numbers over the ship's loud-speaker: "Seven . . . six . . . five . . . four . . ." Each crew-man checked his instrument console. A maze of lights danced and winked. All the lights on the consoles glowed green, everything in the rocketship was in working order.

"Three . . . two," came the blockhouse countdown, "one . . . zero!" The rockets cut in, but the XX-1 did not move.

Now the crew members counted the next ten seconds to themselves. They were the long ten seconds during which the spaceship remained on its pad with rockets roaring. During this time final tests were made in the blockhouse, tests that would ensure the ship a safe blast-off.

Down in the sunken, thick-walled blockhouse dial needles quivered and lights flashed. More than a hundred technicians bent breathlessly over their consoles. Periscope observers made a last-moment check of launching pad No. 16's spaceship. Right now the lives of eight crew members depended on the blockhouse launching team.

"Blast off!" The spaceship crew felt their shoulder blades and the backs of their legs being driven into the foam of their acceleration couches. They gritted their teeth and waited as the XX-1's rocket engines spurted flame.

"Clearing pad," a voice said over the cabin speakers. The pilot had flipped the switch, cutting in the voice of the launching officer in the blockhouse. For the next several minutes messages from the blockhouse would be the only way they would learn of their progress. They were power-less to move even a finger. The men could only lie and wait

124

until the acceleration slackened. Pain racked their bodies as XX-1's rockets pushed her faster and faster away from earth.

Good news from the blockhouse—"Blast-off perfect." They were on their way. Their destination lay exactly 221,-463 miles out in space. "Project Moon Walk" scientists had chosen the time when earth's space neighbor was closest to our planet for the spaceship assault. In ten hours they would be prowling about the moon on foot.

Her tail an orange blaze of power, the delta-winged spaceship stormed through the cloud layer and away, pushed by the most powerful rocket engine the world had ever known. The ship was still on automatic control as her rockets tried to break the grip of gravity.

Just as the crewmen's bodies began to feel normal the second-stage rockets cut in. The fiery surge of power threw the men back into their couches and pain contorted their faces. A weight equal to 1,000 pounds "sat" on their bodies; their ribs felt as though they would cave in under the pressure. They lay on their acceleration couches, taking all that gravity could throw at them but they knew that soon its grip would lessen. They were passing through the dangerous, earth-circling band of Van Allen radiation when they felt the third and last stage rockets cut in.

"Seventeen thousand miles and right on course," came the launching officer's voice. XX-1 was still being monitored from the blockhouse.

Gradually the crushing weight that bore down on the crew members faded. The travelers had little time to congratulate themselves, for a new sensation hit them—weightlessness. A few moments ago their bodies weighed half a ton. Now they weighed absolutely nothing.

How long could they stand it? Tests on earth had done their best to simulate the weightlessness feeling, but would what they were about to experience be anything like the tests?

Working carefully, they loosened the straps binding them to their couches to give themselves a bit more freedom of movement. They knew better than to unbuckle the straps entirely, for that would send their weightless bodies floating to the cabin's overhead. The crew permitted weightlessness to do what it wanted to them. This was a lesson that space scientists had learned during many experiments. Don't try to fight weightlessness with your body, that was the secret, but never let it control your brain.

At last the weird sensation left them. One by one the men unbuckled the restraining bands. By pressing levers near his left hand each man adjusted his couch into a seat. The control center radio faded out, they were strictly on their own.

Until now they had not been men in the true sense, for they had done nothing as men. They had just lain bound to their acceleration couches, waiting until gravity stopped beating at their bodies and until they had passed through the weightlessness stage of their flight.

Men were made to do things. And now the crew began to do the tasks they had practiced for so long. They started to fly their spaceship. The eight men settled down to the routine of getting the 65-foot rocket wagon to the moon.

126

The crew and their duties were: Clemens, pilot and captain of the ship; Butler, copilot; Jankowsky, navigator; Kelly, radio-radar; Thaxton, crew chief; Vargas, assistant crew chief; Skarset, general utility man; Heinz, general utility man.

Clemens sent his first radio message back to earth. Trying to keep his voice calm, he said, "Spaceship XX-1 to control center. Speed, 23,000. Distance from earth, 4,200 miles. On course. Over and out."

The crew smiled at the skipper's message. The 23,000-miles-per-hour speed meant that their ship had reached the velocity necessary to break away from the earth's gravity pull. The distance told them they had completed their two swings around earth and were beginning the great curving arc through space that would eventually zero them in on the moon.

They could now take off their G-suits and work at keeping the spacecraft shipshape. Every man had many jobs to do. Skarset and Heinz started a compartment-by-compartment check for leaks in the supermetal hull. Vargas scanned the oxygen-level gauges and took a closer look at the air-rejuvenation machines. One slip-up and the spaceship's snug control cabin would change from a warm, safe compartment to an icy, airless trap. In seconds the eight men would be struggling for their lives thousand of miles out in space.

The XX-1 shuddered from nose to rocket nozzles. A speeding meteoroid had exploded against the ship's meteor shield. Captain Clemens sent two men forward to check for damage. They returned smiling. The tough buffer had warded off the space projectile.

127

According to plan two men, Skarset and Heinz, re-laxed at their duty stations and began to eat their first meal in space. It consisted of dehydrated, high-protein food. The on-duty men studied their instrument con-soles.

Built into the rocketship were two sets of vital equip-ment. One set was in operation while the other remained on standby. If the first broke down, the crew could switch to the second.

Thaxton, the crew chief, was taking note of oxygen levels in the space voyage logbook when the bulkhead he had just been leaning against exploded with an ear-splitting roar. He threw himself to the deck instinctively. A meteoroid had pierced the ship.

"Meteoroid damage!" he yelled. "Forward oxygen sup-ply."

The crew chief lunged for the airtight door, leaped through, and closed the hatch behind him. His action sealed off the oxygen-supply compartment from the rest of the ship. He leaned against the hatch, sucking in precious oxygen.

Vargas and Skarset rushed to him. "You okay, Thax?" they asked.

The chief nodded. "Made it back before all the air was sucked into space."

As the three stepped through the control cabin hatch Kelly shouted, "The radar's been knocked out."

"That figures," said Thaxton; "that piece of space junk must have hit it."

"Air supply normal, skipper," reported Vargas.

128

"Good," said Clemens. "Then the meteoroid didn't pierce all the oxygen cylinders."

"Right," said Butler, the copilot, "but how many are still intact?"

"Won't know until we seal the hole," answered Clemens. "Thaxton and Heinz, suit up."

The two men helped each other into their space suits. They gathered up the required tools and entered the airlock. With Skarset at the airlock controls Thaxton and Heinz opened the outer hatch and crawled outside the spaceship, where they secured nylon lines to steel eyelets alongside the airlock, then looped and fastened the nylon cord around their midriffs to keep them from drifting off into space.

While the spaceship traveled at 23,000 miles per hour the two repairmen walked along the meteoroid guard to the hull puncture. Beyond the stern rocket tubes they could see Earth, a gigantic globe 130,000 miles distant. A beautiful blue haze surrounded her. Behind Earth gleamed the stars, like diamonds in the velvet black of space. The sun burned with a fierce light. The men blessed their luck. The piece of space junk had penetrated the sunny side of their ship. Had it pierced the other, or "night," side they would have had to pack along cumbersome space lamps in order to see what they were doing.

The repairmen didn't stare around for long. They knew they must work swiftly to avoid absorbing too many cosmic rays. Besides, other meteoroids could swish out of nowhere to hit them as they worked.

Expertly they dismantled the damaged radar dish, replac-

129

ing it with a spare from the ship. Then they patched the fist-size hole in the hull, working as they had been taught on mock-up spaceships back on the earth.

Back to the airlock and into the ship they went. As the repairmen squirmed out of their pressure suits they watched the air-pressure gauges. The oxygen level was building up in the damaged compartment.

"Nice going, fellows," said Kelly. "You've got the radar working again."

Skarset opened the airtight hatch to the forward oxygen-supply compartment. He grinned and with his thumb and first finger he made an "O" sign. All oxygen cylinders were intact. The meteoroid had missed them—the emergency was over.

Navigator Jankowsky's lean face frowned in worry. "I don't like the looks of this, skipper," he said, pointing to the radarscope. Sure enough, the rocketship was bending off course. If they continued on their present course they would miss the moon by thousands of miles and drift on out into deep space.

"Take over, Butler," the pilot commanded the copilot. Captain Clemens and Jankowsky did some fast figuring on the plotting table. Finally they both nodded. Clemens took over ship control again. He moved a lever, the portside rockets ignited and fired a short blast. "Switch to auxiliary course recorder," commanded Clemens. Butler pushed a square button. The recorder needle twitched to life and moved quickly to on-course position. Everyone breathed easier.

"Hold her on that course, Butler," the skipper said, "and in six hours we will be knocking on the moon's doorstep."

Jack-of-all-trades Thaxton bent over the No. 1 course recorder. "Weak tube, skipper," he announced. "No wonder the needle couldn't give us a true reading."

"If it hadn't been for Kelly's radar," replied Clemens, "we wouldn't have picked up the error until it was too late." Thaxton inserted a new electronic tube and the course recorder again became operational.

"Moon 15,000 miles," Clemens's deep voice came over the speaker. "Drift, zero. Right on course." Then, later, "Cutting in retro rockets."

Slowing its speed minute by minute, XX-1 circled the moon. Awestruck at being only 200 miles from their destination, the crew gazed at the jagged, weird landscape below. Craters, large and small, and by the thousands, passed beneath their circling ship.

Jankowsky studied his moon maps. "Project Moon Walk" called for them to land close to Copernicus crater.

"Suit up," said Captain Clemens. He wanted the crew to be protected by their pressure suits in case something went wrong and they crash-landed.

"Stand by for landing."

With rockets spurting flame, the ship backed down closer, closer to a flat moon plain ten miles from Copernicus crater.

"Release landing tripods." Skarset pulled a lever and watched through a porthole as the three legs moved into landing position.

"Touchdown!" The chief pilot shut down all rocket power.

They were to explore the moon in shifts. Four men would

131

23. The Moon seen through the telescope during its last quarter.

remain behind in the ship while the other four prowled the lunar surface. The two groups would maintain radio contact. If the explorers got into trouble, the men in the ship would come to their rescue.

The first four—Clemens, Kelly, Thaxton and Vargas—passed through the airlock, climbed down the ladder, and sank up to their boottops in gritty moon dust. They were the first men to set foot on the moon.

The moon-suited group moved out across the plain, walking as though on eggs. Before long they learned how much muscle to use for moon walking. Gradually the weak lunar gravity no longer bothered them. They had developed their "lunar legs."

132

Single file, five paces between, the men set out for a raw upthrust of jagged rock half a mile away. Vargas studied the thermometer strapped to his moon suit. "It's 214 degrees hot," he reported. Although the men knew that it would be hot on the moon, still they found it hard to believe the temperature was that high because their moon suits shut out the sun's cruel heat. Protected and refrigerated by their moon clothing, they walked along in a 65-degree temperature.

Since the moon has no atmosphere it cannot ward off the sun's direct rays. For the same reason it cannot hold the sun's heat, and in its shadows the temperature drops to 243 degrees below zero. During the long, two-week lunar night the mercury plunges much lower.

The three men behind Clemens stopped in their tracks. A puff of dust seemed to explode about the pilot. He disappeared. The men rushed forward, one, forgetting the weak gravity pull, found himself leaping as high as a pole vaulter.

"Easy, men." It was the voice of Clemens coming to them over the two-way intercom. "I'm all right."

They spotted his helmeted head through the settling dust cloud. He was covered to his neck in moon dust. The others pulled him free. "I must have dropped into a crevasse," the pilot said. "There must be thousands of them radiating out from the craters."

For the next two hours the four men busied themselves with specially assigned tasks. Vargas did measuring; he took readings of cosmic rays, recorded falling meteorites, temperatures, and so on. Thaxton broke off rock specimens

133

while Clemens took samplings of moon dust and made test borings in the solid rock surfaces. Kelly kept in constant radio contact with the rocketship, and took pictures.

After working for two hours the men filed back to the ship. The others now took their walk. No one felt tired. Excitement and curiosity overwhelmed any sign of weariness. The earthlings even forgot to eat. All they could do was look, point, and stare some more.

Almost before the eight men realized it take-off time was at hand. They inspected their ship from stem to stern. Reluctantly they turned to the business of blasting off for home.

The ship's rockets responded perfectly. XX-1 blasted off in a cloud of moon dust and rocket exhaust. Each of the eight astronauts felt that he would soon return for a longer, closer look at the earth's waterless, heatless, soundless, fascinating neighbor.

Still excited over the adventure of having strolled around on the moon, the crew watched the earth loom larger on the rocketship's radar. Then talk fell off, and they remembered the soon-to-come agony of re-entry. The most dangerous parts of the entire trip were approaching: the two passes they had to make around the earth in order to slow down; and the landing itself.

"All hands into pressure suits," ordered Clemens. Skarset inspected the escape capsule. Then, minutes later, Skipper Clemens's voice sounded in their G-suit helmet earphones. "All hands to re-entry stations."

The pilot guided the incoming spaceship into its first

global sweep. Even though securely strapped to their couches, the crew members' bodies quivered under the ship's jarring as it skipped across the top of the earth's air blanket just as a flat rock stutters across a pond.

Pilot and copilot sought to master the XX-1's finger-tip controls. A false move at the control panel could send the delta-winged craft on a steep and fatal plunge into the atmosphere.

To a man the crew seemed to be having trouble with the pressure-suit temperature-control valves. They fumbled to turn more cool air into their suits. The heat level kept rising. Their minds grew hazy under the pounding of re-entry deceleration forces. Heat sucked the moisture from their mouths. Their ship was burning up, they were sure of it.

Heinz spun the cabin refrigeration valve until the "reefer" valve showed half open.

"Re-entry heat building higher." The skipper's words triggered Heinz into turning the auxiliary reefer valve wide open. Sweat still poured off the men's bodies. They knew that outside their cabin the nose of their ship glowed like a red-hot poker.

Eight bodies slammed backward against the rubber couches. The retro rockets cut in full power. The men gave silent thanks to the retros—for without them the XX-1 would have flamed its way down through the atmosphere like a shooting star.

Kelly, the radio operator, kept up a constant dialogue with the Space Base. One more swing around earth and they would have slowed up enough to land. Blast off in Florida and set down in California, that was the plan.

"Air speed, 4,050, and dropping," announced the pilot. "Height, 89 miles. Space Base, 3,500 miles due east."

They were swishing high above the Pacific.

"Space Base calling rocketship XX-1." Kelly was piping the base radio right into the cabin. "We have you on our radar. Our computer figures you at height, correct and speed, correct. Over."

The California coastline flashed below. Clemens nosed the delta-winged craft still lower. XX-1 now traveled at airplane speed. The men could see Los Angeles sprawling to the south.

"Space Base, dead center," announced Clemens. Butler lowered the sturdy landing gear. XX-1 circled the base's 12-mile-long dried-up lake bed. For landing purposes the ship had become just another high-speed rocket plane.

The desert base teemed with black specks. At 2,000 feet the crew saw that the specks were people. Thousands of people had come to the Mojave Desert base to see their return.

Clemens started the slanting approach to the long, wide, flat lake bed. An almost-human squeal echoed in the ship's cabin as the huge landing skids hit ground.

At that moment there came into each crew member's mind the thought, We never would have made it but for those many unsung volunteers before us.

The eight men unscrewed their helmets. In their space suits they resembled men from the moon, which is exactly what they were. And they crawled down out of Spaceship XX-1 to the welcome roar of the crowd thundering in their ears like space rockets.

136